"What on the surface appea
and all its general rubbish, is in
book. Underneath is an aching s.   .... p....... journa very
touching. The sadness contrasted against the raw wit is a clever
device and makes for a highly readable book, albeit one that stops
you in your tracks every now and then as the point is driven
home."

"An engaging comedic story. Fascinating characters. Rich
imagery. Polished writing. Brilliant wit."

"It takes a very intelligent mind to be able to examine oneself
with such humor and skill. Terrific story -- both amusing and
vulnerable - a true pleasure to read."

"Refreshing to read such a candid and amusing tale. Observing
one's life at times can be mundane but you've side-stepped that with
your approach."

"Hilarious...life is stark, but your voice makes situations,
mundane or mean, laughable."

"A hilarious and empathic rant. I think there are a lot of
prospective readers out there who would identify with your anti-
hero."

"This finely crafted novel is a pleasure to read. I especially like
the humour and observations on life. Well paced, well written and
the use of imagery is excellent."

"Really, really good, funny and wonderfully written."

"Reader Meets Author is exquisitely both charming and
excruciating."

"The anger is done well without being too overwhelming and
there is a definite wit and sense of humor that makes it all work.
This is different from anything out there with just the right blend of
anger, humor, wit and whine to make the narrator sympathetic."

READER MEET AUTHOR

N. S. Calcutt

Britain's Next
BESTSELLER

First published in 2016 by:

Britain's Next Bestseller
An imprint of Live It Publishing
27 Old Gloucester Road
London, United Kingdom.
WC1N 3AX

www.britainsnextbestseller.co.uk

All enquiries should be addressed to Britain's Next Bestseller.

ISBN 978-1-910565-68-1 (pbk)

Printed in Poland

To my mother

Supporter List

Charlotte Crowton, Chris Wild, Paula France, Steven Patrick, Kate Lee, Yves Altana, Susan Nicholson, André Leão, Emma Lees, Christopher Orme, Shelley Butler, Nev Rogers, Donna Bishop, Lynda Whittaker, Graham Miller, Claire Elam, John Wood, Stefan Krix, Patricia Sparham, Ann Marie Jackson, Stephen Dickson, Graham Chard, Julie Nash, David Dawkins, Andrew Males, Simon McKenna, Lynsey Williams, Steven Jackson, Raynor Vernon, Kristy Gallagher, Lesley Kelson, Nicola Harrison, Julie Rogers, Caroline Boddy, Sara Rowlands, Laura Gavin, Em @kizimiaz, Mags Burke, Dan Burke, Nigel Jepson, Hannah Saunders, Allison Arekion, Phill Gatenby, Michaela Edwards, Hilary White, Jimmy Bishop, Kathy Caine, Julie Hamill, Grant Lewis, Rachel Porter, Laura Green, Altug Tekin, Clare Hajewskyj, Lee Griffiths, Claire Walsh, Cath McCartan, Michelle Lewin, Rachel Davies, Mike Coy, Toni Sutton, Joanne Lloyd, Katie Webb, Janice Ferneyhough, Stephen Acreman, Corinna Sissons, Neil Wood, Charlotte Holden, Sadie Scrubber, Michelle Fitzpatrick, Sophie Jade Williams, Mike France, Derek Reid, Louise Marshall, Mike Walker, Sue Taylor, Stuart Thomas, Kevin Rankin, Guy Burke, Mark Newland, Karen Mills, Sarah Reid, Denton West End Community Library, Andy Barnett, Brian Forbes, Natalie Adams, Alex Crowton, Paul Cooper, Jac Murray, Michelle (Mish) Sharples, Chris Quirk, Mari Brazier,

Maureen Burslem, Karen Atkins, Caroline Lindsay, Mike Ruane, Russell Thornton, Kelly Rae Bremer, Inge Kersten, Trish Jukes, Neil Newby, Jane Murphy, Kathleen Smith, Richard France, Sue "Princess of Fife" McIntosh, Rachel Smith, Jeni Johnson, Antony Hoyle, Claire Johnston, Frances Arthurs, @redorbrownsauce, Pim Van Heuven, Benn Sanderson, Lyndsey Wilson, Lynda Susan, Janine Hewling, Jane Crawford, Louise Phillips, Anthony Kinsey, Angela Frawley, Melody Redhead, Paul Saunders, Matthew Mills, Juan Manuel Ruiz Sánchez, Joanna Yates, Malcolm McDowell, Hayley Graham, Dave Lee, Sue Halliday, Lucy Batchelor and Jennifer Barber.

Acknowledgements

I would like to thank everyone who has contributed to getting this book published – in particular the support of virtual strangers whose kindness has been most humbling. Huge thanks to Charlotte Crowton for marketing, editing and encouragement and to Martin Hunt for his proof reading skills. Thanks to Yves Altana and John Wood of The Chrysalids for their support and the use of the amazing track 'My Heart is Where my Home Is' for the promotional video. Love and thanks to close family and friends including Mum, Dad, Susan, Henry, Molly, Emma, Dave, BB, Fran, Lynda, Kenny, Paula, Joanne, Sue, Kristy, Louise, Hilary, Janice, Susan, Liz, Kate, Ann-Marie, Mel, Clare, Natalie and many more. I will always be grateful for the music of Morrissey and The Chameleons, and the highs and many lows of watching Manchester City FC. This book is dedicated to my mum and the city of Manchester.

Chapter One

January 6th, 1972.

A date that heralded my entrance into this world and, to be honest, not a great date to have a birthday. Now don't get me wrong, I'm definitely no believer in fate, or karma, or predetermined destinies or any of that crap, but being born on that date pretty much set a precedent for the rest of my life. You see, throughout my life, I feel like I've had an inordinate amount of bad luck.

Take this morning, for example. I'd decided to go and grab a coffee on my way in to work. I wasn't even that bothered about getting a coffee, if you must know, but sometimes I like to take a slight detour to delay the soul destroying daily ritual of sitting in the office. There are loads of coffee shops around town these days – I don't think there were any when I was younger. It's really expensive too and it's crazy but everyone seems to be idiotic enough to stump up over two quid for a cup of coffee – me included.

Anyway, while I was stood in the queue in that coffee shop, I'd decided to order a croissant with my drink. I was standing second in line to be served, watching carefully as the shop assistant began to pick up croissant after croissant with plastic tongs and put them in a paper bag. They were for the middle-aged woman with badly-dyed hair who was stood in front of me in the queue. I guessed she must have been getting a load for people she worked with, or something. Well, just when I'd resigned myself to having to make do without that bastard croissant, the shop assistant put the tongs down, leaving one still remaining on the shelf. Safe in the knowledge that there were no other customers between me and that croissant, I allowed myself to revel in a rare victory. There was an almost tangible sense of jealousy from those queuing behind me as I directed the assistant to the solitary pastry. My stroke of luck would make this particular breakfast taste even sweeter.

"Oops, I'm sorry love. I've dropped it on the floor. Do you want anything else?"

For fuck's sake.

Now I'm no great believer in the concept of luck *per se,* but I swear that kind of thing happens to me every day. Just when I think something's gonna go my way, no matter how small, life takes a big run up and kicks me in the balls.

January 6th

Epiphany

The twelfth day of Christmas

In the United Kingdom, this is traditionally the day when the festivities end. It's the day when the holiday period is over. Begrudgingly, people return to work and children return to school. It's the day when the Christmas tree and the decorations *have* to come down. It's the day when the party is *officially* over. As I said, not a great date to have a birthday. The psychological impact of spending each and every birthday tearing down tinsel, dismantling the artificial tree, and generally returning the house to its previous dour state, *cannot* be underestimated. And that's not the only downside….

"Here you are love, that's for Christmas *and* your birthday".

One present. Thanks a fucking lot, Aunty Betty. Try giving someone a gift in June and telling them it's their Christmas *and* birthday present. Now I'm sure loads of poor bastards with birthdays around Christmas suffer with the same injustice, but January 6th is just the worst. Try drumming up support to join you in starting a celebration on January 6th. It's the weekend after New Year's Eve. Everybody's miserable and everybody's skint. And if you *do* happen to make enough people feel guilty enough to venture into town, you'll find that every bar is like a fucking ghost town. Some celebration.

From listening to me whine on about birthdays, you'd think I enjoyed them or something. The fact is I don't. I'm in my thirties now and I don't even feel the slightest inclination to celebrate birthdays anymore. To be honest, the only reason I *have* celebrated them in the past is because it's one of those occasions like New Years Eve, when everyone insists you *should* be happy and join in with the revelry.

I've always hated New Year's Eve – even more than birthdays. I don't even get what it is we're supposed to be celebrating. I don't find the passing of another year as we inch towards death something to get ecstatic about. It's bad enough staying at home on New Year's Eve and turning on the TV to watch loads of awful people pretending they're having the best time ever. It's even worse being out in a bar or club and being surrounded by those people. The dreaded countdown to midnight followed by the fake euphoria as complete morons whoop and cheer to celebrate I don't bleeding know what.

Those New Year's Eve parties must be dreaded even more by the female population. As sex-starved teenagers, me and my friends knew that the strike of midnight at New Year in a bar or a club was a godsend. It was the one time of the year that you could approach total strangers and demand an embrace – the perfect excuse to get close to a pretty girl who would ordinarily grimace at sharing the same building with you. With outstretched arms and a proclamation of 'Happy New Year!' no woman could decline – it was an unwritten law. Plenty of guys made the most of that opportunity and spent the first few minutes of the New Year enthusiastically snogging and groping girls. I never got more than a hug and a peck on the cheek. My nervous smile probably made me look deranged. That grin coupled with my lack of conversation (aside from repeating 'Happy New Year!' over and over again) meant even dousing myself in Brut 33 never helped me. Maybe it's the real reason I hate that time of year so much.

At least with birthdays I can understand the rationale for wanting to celebrate, even though the theory behind it is pretty fucking flawed if you ask me. Don't get me wrong, it's great to receive gifts and stuff, but the older I've become, the more I've thought that birthdays are a pretty miserable milestone. And not just because the presents dry up, the older you get. I distinctly remember at Christmas time and birthdays, watching my dad open his pitifully small ensemble of gifts and thinking 'you poor bastard' as he tried to feign excitement at another pack of black socks or some scented talcum powder. Unbeknownst to me at that time, just like the onslaught of nasal hair, this would be another unavoidable experience of getting old.

The thing about birthdays, and life in general for that matter, is people's attitude towards them. I mean as far as we're aware, the facts of life are that we are born, we live for a finite length of time, and then we die. To the best of *anyone's* knowledge, *that* is fucking *that*. Now you would think with that knowledge on board, we would spend the majority of our days frantically running around in circles and crying, vainly trying to come to terms with the fact that there will be a day when we no longer exist and that everything will carry on without us. You might also rationally think that armed with the knowledge that we have such a short existence on this planet; we would appreciate how precious each day is and spend every waking moment living life to the full. Yet we're quite happy to while away our valuable time playing Sudoku and watching *The Bill*.

My dad has said a lot to me in my life, but one thing in particular sticks in my mind. To be honest, and this probably doesn't sound too nice, I've spent a lot of my life avoiding conversations with my dad. The thing is, he'd start talking to you about something or other, but it would take him about a month to finish. He'd take these long pauses between sentences where you'd be desperate to jump in but just as you'd go to, he'd start off talking again. I swear you could start a conversation with my dad clean shaven and end up with a full beard by the time he'd finished.

This thing that my dad said, (and I didn't take much notice of it at the time), was that the older you get, then the quicker the years go by. I thought it was a load of bollocks at the time and, scientifically speaking, I suppose it *is* a load of bollocks, but when you get older, years do start to zip by a lot quicker than ever before. It's not even as though you can enjoy the years as you get older either. As each birthday passes, my body deteriorates and my 'get-up-and-go' just seems to have 'got-up-and-gone.'

I remember when I was younger, probably about 13 or so, sitting down in front of the TV with the family. We were watching *Coronation Street* or something, so it must have only been a short time after seven-thirty. When I looked across at my dad he was slumped with his head back and mouth wide, snoring away. Fast asleep and it wasn't even eight o'clock. At the time I just shook my head in pity, but the thing is, I'm not even forty now and if I start watching a film at ten p.m., then there's no fucking way I'll get to see the end. I spend the whole day working and then I end up falling asleep in the scant time that I get to enjoy myself.

I suppose it's probably best that I don't dwell on the subject of aging and death too much and just enjoy the time that I've got left. Although it does make me vomit thinking about the precious time we have on Earth and the knowledge that I've spent a healthy percentage of it masturbating and watching *Coronation Street*. Not at the same time obviously.

The reality for most people is that they spend most of their waking life at a place they don't want to be, doing something they don't want to do, surrounded by people they don't want to be with. And the fucked up thing is that everybody just goes along with it – me included. It's like we all sign up to the biggest fucking con without even realising it.

"Hey, have I got a deal for you! Listen to this! The first sixteen years of your life – they're yours! I'm not asking for anything. And I'll tell you what I'm gonna do – you can even have another five after that, although it'll probably cost ya. So you've had twenty-one years to do whatever you like! Pretty good, eh?"

"But from what I understand aren't the baby and toddler years pretty useless? I mean I won't be able to walk, talking's pretty limited and I'm totally reliant on someone else to decide what I do. And won't I spend a lot of the time crying and sitting around in my own shit?"

"Well ... that is true I suppose. But on the flipside you'll find the slightest thing fucking hilarious. Anyway you'll be talking and walking around and wiping your own arse in no time."

"By no time, you mean about three or four years."

"Whatever."

"Ok, I suppose. But aren't the years after that spent with me remaining totally dependent on someone else?

And won't I be forced to be in some kind of educational institution for pretty much the majority of the time? And won't I have to cope with my body changing and deal with all the heartache and emotional trauma that comes with that? And won't I spend my whole teenage years under the illusion that I know it all, when I'll actually know fuck all and that'll lead to loads of embarrassing situations that I'll always remember?"

"Hmm ... let's not dwell on that, and instead move onto a few other things that I need to get straight. Ok, you're twenty-one; the world's your oyster. Here's the deal. You can do whatever you please. But you'll need somewhere to live, things to eat, things to wear, things to entertain you. You won't be able to exist without food, water, gas, electricity. All this stuff costs money. You'll be able to get money to pay for all these things and all you have to do is agree to turn up at a specified place and do a specified task for somebody else for about seven hours a day, five days a week for approximately forty-seven weeks of the year."

"Get lost!"

"Wait a minute. C'mon, it's only about thirty per cent of your waking days each year. The rest is yours! Just think – not only do you get the two days out of the week, but you also get every night to yourself!"

"Well … Ok then. How many years do I have to do that for?"

"Until you're at least sixty. Maybe a few years more."

"Forget it!"

"No, wait. So say you stop working at sixty – the rest of your life is all yours!"

"And how long am I likely to live?"

"Dunno. Could be anytime – you might even live to a hundred or so!"

"Wait a minute! That's still the majority of my life I'd be signing away. And I might only live till sixty-five and just get a couple of years to enjoy myself. Man, I could even die in my fifties and get nothing!"

"But … you might live to be a hundred! Although by that stage you'll probably be back to not walking much, being totally reliant on someone else and spending hours sat in your own shit."

And in my mind, when it's put like that, then the harsh realisation is that life *is* a gigantic con. Of course you could choose *not* to work, but then you're totally reliant on support from the capitalist society you're choosing *not* to take part in. It's absolutely crazy.

Anyway, I bet you're probably thinking 'What has this bastard got to moan about? He doesn't realise how lucky he is!' And *obviously* everything is relative….

"Next please."

"Man, that guy got a rough deal. So what have you got for me?"

"Lemme see … Hmm … ok. I'm gettin' a lot more visibility on this one. Ok … you'll be born with a heroin addiction … to a prostitute. You'll be physically and sexually abused by her boyfriend … before dying of your injuries in your third year."

"What?"

"Ok, ok. I know it doesn't sound too glamorous. But

hey, at least you don't have to wait around until you're a teenager like that last sap before you get the sex and drugs action."

So yeah, like I said, I know everything's relative and me moaning on about my life and birthdays and other stuff pales into insignificance with what some people have to face in their lives. But hey, I'm gonna carry on anyway....

Chapter Two

I can't remember how old I was when my mum died. I guess I must have been about twenty or twenty-one, but I seriously *cannot* remember. I have an *awful* memory but something like that I *should* remember. The thing is I tend to bury my head in the sand when anything bad happens and pretend to myself that it *hasn't* happened. I guess we all bury our head in the sand about certain things – like, for example, the advent of death that I was talking about. But I do it with lots of stuff. To be honest, it's with anything that makes me feel sad.

Some people are completely the opposite and have to go on and on about bad things that have happened to them. I guess it must make them feel better, but I can't understand how going on about something miserable can help you feel better. It's not like anyone else wants to hear about it either. I mean, why would *anybody* feel the need to burden someone else with their problems? Some people think you want to know *everything* about them, when seriously, why would you? Even, for example, if you see someone and you say 'Hi. How are you?' When you ask that, you're just after something in response like 'I'm fine thanks. How are you?' and then you can move on from there. But some people start saying things like 'Well, I've not been so well recently and blah blah fucking blah.' Those people just love talking about themselves. You've just gotta sit there listening whilst pretending to look bothered with intermittent nods of the head. It really gets on my nerves. I mean, even if I'd just been hit by a ten-ton truck and was minutes away from death, I'd still just reply, 'I'm fine thanks. How are you?'

On the whole, I'd say my mum was pretty much the exact opposite of my dad. She was so laidback and let me and my sister do whatever we wanted, within reason. I guess I've never really liked talking about her before and I don't know why I am now. I suppose it's easier just writing stuff down. It makes me sad talking about her though and, like I said earlier, why would anyone want to listen anyway? I sure as hell wouldn't want to hear someone else droning on about a dead relative. I promise I'll try and keep it short.

My mum was really active when she was younger. She used to enjoy walking everywhere, and she even played for a women's football team. You should see how she looks on some of the old photographs my sister has. There's this one black and white photo where she's stood outside a toy shop. Pemberton's, I think it was called. I remember she used to work there for a while when I was a kid. It was great 'cos occasionally she'd bring me home these Dinky Toy cars. I had quite a collection after a while although I haven't a clue what happened to them all. Anyhow, in the photo she's got a white bag in one hand and she's smiling at whoever's taking the picture. She's quite skinny and she's wearing this short, polka-dot dress; she looks really great. I haven't got any photographs of her. Thinking about it, I don't really have photographs of anything. I suppose I should have a photograph of her now she's not around anymore. People would probably expect me to have one in the house somewhere but I know it'd just make me sad 'cos I'd see it and be constantly reminded of how she's not here anymore. Sometimes I think I might like to have that black and white picture of her smiling though.

The whole point about photographs is that they're supposed to capture a particular moment in time. In my eyes though, those pictures are totally fake. When people have a camera pointed at them, they're *forced* to smile and pose for that photograph. It doesn't matter if you're feeling miserable or having a dreadful time, you've gotta look into that camera lens and smile. For those few seconds, you've gotta fake your emotions and that's what will be captured forever on film. That's why I can't stand having my picture taken. I really can't fake my emotions. I find it hard to smile unless I have a genuine reason to smile. I can hold a fake smile for maybe a second but by the time the button has been pressed on the camera my face has usually slipped and I end up grimacing and looking like I'm having a fucking stroke or something.

Apparently my mum was walking home with a friend of hers one day when a car suddenly mounted the pavement and knocked them both down. The driver was drunk, so my mum said. I never really asked her about it much 'cos, like I said, I don't like talking about stuff that makes me sad. She never died from her injuries or anything, but mentally she went rapidly downhill from there. She couldn't get around too well after that accident. I mean, she could still walk about, but nowhere near as much as she previously could. She'd get tired really quickly and had to have a lot of physiotherapy, and she also put on a lot of weight. It must have really gotten to her, especially with having been so active and skinny beforehand, and she started to suffer with depression. And I guess in turn that's what led to the stints of alcoholism. I don't know *exactly* when it happened as me and my sister would have been quite young around this time, but at some stage my mum and dad split up. I don't know why they split up and I don't wanna know. I don't think I could handle knowing either of them was to blame.

Before they split up, we used to all live together in this house in Moss Side, in the south of Manchester. It was quite a big house and it had a nice front garden too. We weren't really well off or anything like that, but I think we could afford a house like that because it wasn't a very nice area of the city. I remember this Asian guy in the local shop had his head all bandaged up one day as a result of some nutcase who attacked him with a machete during a robbery. I told you I have a really bad memory but I can still remember the odd thing from my childhood. Lovely things like machete attacks.

Even now, whenever I think of that nice garden we had, the only memory I have is *typically* a fucking bad one. I remember going into the garden one morning and finding bits of an old LP scattered all about the lawn. Although the record was all smashed up, I could still recognise it from the pieces of the sleeve. It was the cover of a record that belonged to my mum. I think it was called *Best of the Stylistics* – it was something by

The Stylistics anyway. I gathered all the bits up in my hands and ran back into our house to show them to my mum.

When I held out my hands and revealed those fragments of broken vinyl, she got really upset. She didn't actually say anything from what I recall, she just had this terribly sad look on her face and I could see tears welling up in her eyes. Makes me upset even now to think about seeing her react like that. It turns out my mum or dad had recently had an argument with the family from across the road. They'd previously borrowed that LP from my mum and it seemed one of them must have smashed it into bits after the argument, and thrown all the pieces into our front garden. It was a pretty fucking malicious thing to do, if you ask me.

Back then, I couldn't really do anything to make my mum feel better. I feel rubbish that it's only now I have a decent job and could afford to get her another copy of that album by The Stylistics or a copy of any other record she wanted. I'm not amazingly well paid or anything, but I'm pretty comfortable I suppose and I could have helped out with money and bought her any stuff she wanted. Giving her that record and buying her nice things might have made me stop thinking about that day and how upset she was when I gave her those bits of broken vinyl. She's dead now though so, like I say, I feel like shit.

I remember one time when I did try to make my mum happy with a gift, and looking back, I pretty much fucked that up too. I was in my teens, I think, and I'd been living with my mum in a house which belonged to my uncle. He used to teach English abroad, in the

Middle East mainly. I guess he used to earn shed loads of cash doing it, 'cos he'd buy up all these houses back in Manchester for investment purposes. My mum hadn't worked since she'd met my dad, and when they split up I don't think she *could* work, what with the physical and psychiatric problems and all. She never had any money to speak of, so my uncle used to let her stay in these houses he owned. She used to move about a bit 'cos he'd sometimes decide to sell the one she had and would re-house her in another. He's a pretty good guy and was a good brother to her.

Anyway, as I said, my mum didn't have much money. I remember that this one particular Christmas time, we'd agreed not to get each other a present, being that neither of us had any cash. Despite that conversation, I thought it would be a nice thing to do if I went and got her a present anyway. I figured it would be an even bigger surprise given that we'd had that agreement. My mum was a really big fan of Cliff Richard and I'd seen this new video of his advertised on TV. I couldn't see the attraction of Cliff Richard myself at all, although I do quite like 'Wired for Sound' and 'Devil Woman'. I probably wouldn't admit that to anyone I liked though. My mum had pretty good taste in music otherwise. She had even started getting into the music of The Smiths and Morrissey a few years before she died. I vividly remember her telling me how much she loved 'Back to the Old House.' It's a beautiful song but, looking back, it probably wasn't the most uplifting music I could have introduced to someone with suicidal tendencies.

I remember feeling a bit embarrassed going into HMV in town to buy the Cliff Richard video. I felt like

I should explain to the shop assistant that it wasn't actually for me and that it *was* in fact a generous gesture for the benefit of a beloved older relative. I didn't say a thing though, mainly 'cos any embarrassment was somewhat masked by the warm feeling I was getting at the thought of my mum's face after opening the gift. But there was also the realisation that the guy behind the counter obviously wouldn't give a fuck *who* it was for. I was pretty pleased with myself for getting that gift though. I remember the boxed, plastic packaging contained two videotapes – I think one had loads of music videos on and the other was a concert he'd done.

I wrapped it up when I got back home, and that Christmas Eve I waited until she'd gone to bed before leaving it in the front room on the armchair that she always sat on. She was pretty pleased with it in the morning, I guess, but the first thing she said was that she hadn't got me anything. I knew she wouldn't have, not 'cos she was mean or anything, but just 'cos I knew she didn't have much money, and I really didn't care anyway. The thing is I'd been so looking forward to that moment, to watching the surprise on her face at getting a present and seeing her in high spirits 'cos of that Cliff Richard video. But it was obvious that she just felt really bad I'd got her a present and she'd not got her son anything in return. So you see, I tried to make her happy and I ended up making her feel bad about herself. I always seem to make the wrong decisions in life whatever I do. I try to do things right, but it nearly always fucks right up.

The family from across the road weren't too nice, as you've probably already guessed. They were pretty rough, if you know what I mean. This lanky, bald guy lived there with his wife and children. The husband and wife were both really ugly and I'm not just saying that 'cos of how they upset my mum. The guy was an awkward, geeky looking type with a head that looked too large for his skinny frame. I remember he always wore these really large glasses with black rims. He wasn't completely bald and he had tufts of hair around each ear that bald guys sometimes have. It's as if they think that by hanging onto those bits of hair it might encourage the rest of their head to start sprouting again. His wife was even uglier – she was squat and dumpy with matching spectacles and real cruel looking features. That was the thing with both of them – they just looked incredibly mean. They had three kids – two boys and one girl. Their kids were all a few years older than me and as much as I despised them, I couldn't help but feel sorry for them for having such mean, ugly looking parents. Obviously I didn't know then that one day that mean, ugly, dumpy woman would become my step mum and her awful offspring would become my step brothers and sister.

The *fucking* irony.

Chapter Three

Although I can't remember much of my childhood at that house, I do have the odd good memory. I remember waking up in my bed one Sunday morning, with the sunshine glinting through the gaps in my bedroom curtains. I remember hearing the sound of bells ringing outside from the nearby church and I could hear my mum hoovering downstairs and singing along to this Timi Yuro record that was playing on the stereo. That Timi Yuro has a great voice. Really powerful and strong. I couldn't believe it when I found out she was white. She has one of those really deep, soulful voices that send shivers down your spine when she hits certain notes. Anyway, that morning with the church bells and the sunshine through the curtains and the sound of my mum hoovering to Timi Yuro, it all made me feel really happy and content and secure. It's hard to put into words just exactly what I mean. I still like thinking about that morning though.

There's not much else I can remember about the time we lived in that house. Actually, there *are* two other incidents, but they're both pretty embarrassing, to tell you the truth. I suppose I might as well tell you about them though, being that I've told you all that other stuff already. And especially since one of the stories concerns my only foray into the criminal world (unless you count the times I used to throw a tennis ball against the wall of the end house with a flagrant disregard for the '*No Ball Games Allowed*' sign). Looking back it was probably the most ill-devised criminal plan in the history of criminal plans.

I'm two years older than my sister and I must have been about seven or eight at the time of the Great Ice Cream Van Robbery. My sister was really adorable back then. She had this pretty little face and sleek dark brown hair that was cut into this cool bob hairstyle. Even though she's in her thirties now, I still like to think of her as how she was back then, all sweet and innocent with a cute little button nose.

My sister went off the rails a bit as a teenager whereas I was pretty boring, if you really want to know. She used to get up to all kinds of crap and it used to bug me that she still got all the attention, even though she was always doing things to disappoint my dad while I was generally being boring and not doing anything wrong and passing exams and stuff. Fuck, I used to get into trouble even when I'd done *nothing* wrong.

I remember this one time when me, my sister and my dad were supposed to visit my uncle and we had to get a bus all the way across town. It was really busy when we got on the bus and we all had to traipse upstairs in order to get a seat. In those days, everyone could smoke on the top deck and you'd be immersed in a fetid, thick fog after climbing the stairs and reaching the top step. I sat next to my dad on the horrific upholstery that is all the rage on public transport. My sister sat behind us on a seat that appeared to have been the recipient of some bored youth's Stanley knife. After a few minutes, I'd started idly looking around at the other passengers and at the graffiti carved into the seats and inked around the windows. The graffiti was the usual declarations of love between various initialled individuals, alongside an abundance of poorly sketched penises. I remember that in amongst all the vandalism, some wag had scratched the capital 'D' from the *'Dogs Not Allowed'* sign and replaced it with a 'W'. I was only quite young at the time and had scant awareness of racial prejudice, let alone any racist terms, and 'wogs' just seemed like a funny little word to me. I let out a small chuckle and pointed it out to my dad and my sister. Instead of receiving high fives all round for being the one to bring this nugget of comedy gold to their attention, I was met with a crack around the head from my father's hand. It *really* fucking stung and the pain, along with the shock of the assault, led to tears streaming down my cheeks. It's not *quite* on the same scale as the Birmingham 6 or the Stefan Kiszko case, but I still feel a great sense of injustice to this day.

My dad was quite a disciplinarian when I think back. I love him dearly, but I've always held a sort of fearful respect for him. I've tried to cultivate that same sort of feeling in my kids, but to no avail. They don't listen to a bleeding word I say. I guess it's 'cos I spend a lot more time with them than my dad did with me, so they know I'm pretty soft really. I remember if I'd ever done anything wrong that I'd be petrified waiting for my dad to come home. He had quite a fucking temper on him, I can tell you. There was this one occasion when he bollocked me and it was another time when I'd done absolutely fuck all wrong.

When my dad split with my mum and got together

with my step mum, we moved for a short time to this dreary maisonette in Ardwick, an awfully grim part of Manchester. While we were living there, I remember my dad had bought me these brand new black trousers for school. It was quite rare for us to get new clothes as my dad would usually make sure he'd had his money's worth out of anything he'd paid for. This usually resulted in us wearing clothes that were way too small for us and it wasn't unusual for me to feel a cold breeze where my half-mast trousers struggled to meet up with my socks.

Anyhow, I'd been playing football at break time in those brand new black school trousers and remember chasing for the ball. The next thing I knew, I'd tripped up and gone head over heels across the ground. I tripped over a lot as a kid, thanks to these long, gangly legs I have. The playground floor was made of this really hard grey concrete and it hurt loads when you landed on it. I was left sat on the floor, looking down at my knee, which was stinging with pain due to the bloodied joint now poking out of a hole in my trousers. My fucking *brand new* black school trousers. The *first* fucking day I was wearing them. Straight away, I forgot all about the pain and just thought about how mad my dad was gonna be.

I didn't say a word when I got home and I was dreading the whole evening. I knew we'd be sat in the living room in front of the TV, as usual, and I knew he'd notice that hole in my trousers. I came up with an ingenious plan to avoid detection which involved me keeping one hand over my wounded knee at all times. It takes a lot of fucking concentration, I can tell you, to do something so ridiculously unnatural as keeping one hand over your knee for a whole three hours. I got away with it that first night, but it was only postponing the inevitable. Sure enough, one lapse of concentration the following evening and he was onto it like a fucking shot. He was really mad and sent me straight to my room and told me I was grounded. That was pretty fucking laughable because I never left the bleeding house anyway, apart from going to school. He may as well have told me I wasn't allowed to smoke cigars whilst juggling on a unicycle anymore. And *for fuck's sake* – it was an accident anyway.

I think the reason that trouser incident still sticks in my mind – apart from the fact that my selective memory loves remembering all the shit times in my life – is not the unfairness of it all (although I think you'll agree there was a grave injustice committed that day), it's more to do with what happened the following day.

Typically, me and my sister would walk to my dad's shop after school and he would drive us home afterwards. My dad is a hairdresser, not one of those swanky, trendy hairdressers, but a traditional old-style barber. It's the type of place that's either frequented by bald pensioners who just turn up for a chat while my dad cuts thin air above their heads; or parents who drag their kids along 'cos it's really cheap. Let's put it this way, I'm not expecting to inherit a vast fortune from the business when he dies. It's crazy though, some people would pay their one pound fifty, or whatever it was, and expect some really trendy hairstyle. I swear my dad only knew two hairstyles – you could either have a crew cut or a short back and sides.

It cracks me up when I think about this one time when this young hoodlum came into the shop asking to have the Nike symbol shaved into the side of his hair. I don't know what my dad thought a Nike symbol looked like but what he shaved onto that poor fucker's head sure as hell bore no resemblance to that Nike swoosh. What the hell did he expect though by assuming a sixty-odd year old man would know how to do that hairstyle? My dad may have had a certificate on his wall from the Hairdressing Institute from about eighteen hundred and eight but you can be pretty certain he hadn't been taught to shave the logos of global corporations onto people's heads. What kind of halfwit wants to walk around with stuff shaved into their hair anyway? It fucking beats me, I can tell you.

The day after I'd been grounded, my dad drove me and my sister home as usual, once he'd finished up in the shop. We spent a lot of time hanging about at that barber shop. I'd regularly waste time reading the old papers and magazines that were left for customers, or I'd just nosey about around the place. My uncle always had 'The Sun' newspaper delivered, so I'd usually spend a few minutes each day feasting my eyes on the topless model on page three. The Ladies' side of the shop was full of magazines like 'Woman's Own', 'Woman' and 'The People's Friend' and, even though I knew I didn't *quite* fit their target audience, I'd typically while away a bit of time looking through them. They were mostly full of recipes and knitting patterns and other such crap, but the best part of those magazines was the problem pages 'cos they'd typically be full of eye-opening topics for a naïve young adolescent male like me. Still, as much as I enjoyed the letters in those magazines, and the tales of lop-sided breasts, heavy menstruation and impotent husbands, I'd usually swiftly return to the comfort of Sam Fox, resplendent with her inane grin and bounteous knockers.

I remember they had this big steel cabinet in the back of the shop that was full of combs and lotions and other hairdressing paraphernalia. Alongside all the spare combs and brushes, I remember there was also a huge box of condoms in that steel cabinet too. I didn't have a fucking clue what they were at the time but looking back it seems that old 'something for the weekend' thing must have actually gone on. I can't quite understand the correlation between getting your hair done and purchasing a pack of prophylactics. Seems a bit much too, having to have your hair cut every time you wanted to have sex.

Sometimes we'd help my dad by sweeping up all the bits of freshly shorn hair from the shop floor, before he locked up and we'd leave. The discarded hair would be predominantly grey, reflecting the bulk of my dad's clientele, and it would be quite a job removing it from the nooks and crannies around the cabinets and public seating. Not that we'd get paid for helping out *at all*. My dad has always been extremely frugal. In other words, he's a bit of a tight bastard. The only money we ever got out of my dad was ten pence a week pocket money. Now you're probably thinking that ten pence isn't a lot of money these days, but I can tell you it wasn't a bleeding lot in those days either. We'd usually blow it all on sweets – yeah, that's right the whole damn ten pence.

We used to get our sweets from this shop that was next door-but-one to my dad's shop. It was run by this nice old couple by the name of 'Middleton'. The glass door was always marked with the sweaty handprints of children eager to enter, and when you walked in you'd hear the familiar ring of the bell above the door. Down the right hand side of the shop there were shelves of toys, while the opposite side was filled with jar upon jar of sweets. It was like a crack den for kids. Kola Kubes, Sherbet Lemons, Sarsaparilla Tablets, Strawberry Bonbons; they'd all sit enticingly lined up against the glass cabinet. I'd spend ages agonising over whether to get a 'Wham!' bar or ten pence worth of Kola Kubes. My 'dealer' was the curly, grey-haired Mrs Middleton and I used to stand there nervously waiting for my fix as she'd pour the confectionary onto her scales. The shop isn't there anymore now – I think it's an off licence, or a betting shop, or a tanning salon, or some other non-descript staple of the modern day poverty stricken northern suburb. Mr and Mrs Middleton have probably long since retired to a luxury resort with the proceeds from their ill-gotten gains off the plaque-ridden children of Oldham.

Sometimes we'd ask our dad for bus fare home, instead of waiting around for him, although we'd often spend that on sweets and walk back anyway. More often than not he just made us wait around for him to finish up. That particular day, the day after I'd been grounded, he drove us home to the *beautiful* flat in the *beautiful* maisonette in the *beautiful* part of Manchester I told you about. We had to go up a few flights of stairs to get to our flat and we'd usually run up the stairs while my dad messed about with the car, doing whatever he was doing.

There was a girl who lived on the same floor as we did at the crappy maisonette. I'd seen her a couple of times and we'd even reached the point where we were exchanging smiles. *I know, pretty heavy stuff, eh?* Now, I don't mind admitting that at the time we lived in that maisonette, I didn't really know too much about love or sex, or *anything* about girls for that matter. I was only about eleven or twelve and the only girl I really talked to was my sister, and I didn't even class her as a girl. All I knew was that I quite liked looking at that girl and it made me feel funny inside just thinking about her. She had shoulder-length dark hair and pretty green eyes with these freckles across her nose, and she looked about the same age as me. She was gorgeous.

That day, I bounded up the stairs ahead of my sister. As I turned onto our particular floor, that girl was sat right outside on her doorstep. I remember feeling a bit panicky as I ground to a halt and stood in front of her. I didn't know what the fuck I was doing, if you really want to know, but I remember saying 'Hi' and trying my best to act as 'cool' as possible. Anyway, it seemed to be working 'cos she replied with a 'Hi' and returned my smile. I was feeling really good, really happy, just stood there with that girl. Then it all went wrong. One second I was stood there smiling, doing my 'cool' look, and the next second I heard my dad screaming 'GET INSIDE!' and felt a large arm around my waist as I was hauled off my feet into the air and carried sideways along the rest of the floor and into our flat. There's not really any way you can continue to look cool when you're being carried sideways by your father like a rolled-up carpet across the landing of a maisonette.

Afterwards, I can vividly remember being curled up on my bed and feeling really embarrassed and incredibly angry about how my dad had totally humiliated me. We didn't stay at the maisonette for that much longer and I never saw that girl again. To tell you the truth, I'd have been too embarrassed to look at her even if I had done.

Anyway, I *was* telling you about those two embarrassing memories that I had back from when I lived with my mum, dad and sister. You know, sometimes I think about things that I've done in the past and I can't comprehend for the life of me what possible reason I did them. Don't worry, I'm not about to admit to being some serial killing rapist or anything like that. Although that would probably be less embarrassing than what I'm gonna tell you.

On this particular day, I remember it was quite a pleasant day weather wise and, believe you me; anything other than persistent fucking rain in Manchester is nothing short of a bleeding miracle. Like I said, I must have only been about seven or so at the time, which would have made my sister about five. There was this large park quite close to our house and there would always be an ice cream van parked there, waiting to take advantage of the odd occasion the sun actually managed to make an appearance. That day, I decided that I was gonna treat myself and my sister to an ice cream each. Now, even at that early stage in her life, my sister had realised that there was no fucking way she'd get the money out of my dad for one, so

I was pretty much her only option. I told her to wait patiently nearby and that I'd be back imminently with two ninety-nines.

The only flaw that existed in the preparation to purchase those two ice cream cones was that I didn't actually have *any* money whatsoever. I did have my plan though. Sure, I didn't have any *real*, *actual* money but there was a Monopoly set in my bedroom absolutely over laden with pretend cash. I could use a bright pink five pound note from my board game – *what could possibly go wrong?*

I still to this day cannot understand quite what was going through my mind as I concocted what I must have thought at the time was a flawless strategy. I remember standing patiently in the queue at the ice-cream van and then placing my order once I'd reached the front. After what seemed like an eternity, the ice cream guy inserted a chocolate flake in each of the ice cream scoops and then turned to request payment with a large, hairy outstretched hand. I think it was at that precise moment that it dawned on me that my plan was not going to work. I remember tentatively reaching up with the bright pink note. The bright pink note that looked *abso-fucking-lutely* nothing like legal tender. I may as well have scribbled the queen's face and a big '5' on a Cornish pasty and handed that across. Well, his professionally trained eye managed to somehow rumble my attempted counterfeit scam and I remember he glared at me before I turned and ran, with his angry bellows echoing behind me in the distance. I didn't stop running until I was out of sight and had reached my sister at our designated rendezvous. I had to tell her that we wouldn't be having an ice cream after all.

The last memory that I was gonna tell you about from that house is also embarrassing, although at least this time it isn't anything to do with me doing something idiotic. There was this big house on our street that was next door-but-one to us. It was the end house on the next row from ours and this old couple lived there with their son. The husband and wife were nice, cheery sorts and they got on pretty well with most people on the street. I'd say their son was probably in his thirties and I can't remember what was wrong with him exactly, but he had some kind of physical and mental disability. I don't think it's politically correct anymore to say he was retarded, but anyway that's what he was.

I don't think that the son had many friends to speak of and because he was in a wheelchair and had the mental age of someone a lot younger, his parents were happy for the local kids to come into the house and chat to him. Me and this other boy used to go round there quite regularly and talk to their son. We'd often go up to his room, mainly 'cos he'd have all these great things up there, like model trains and space rockets and other such stuff. I'm pretty sure his parents bought him quite a lot of expensive toys and cool equipment just to keep him happy. I don't think he left that bedroom much, to be honest.

I remember the last time me and my pal went over to their house. It was early one Saturday afternoon and we'd called at the front door, as we regularly did, and his mum and dad answered and were really pleasant, as they always were. They gave us a drink of cordial and told us to go right on up to see their son. He was sat in this chair near to his desk and we just started chatting and playing, as we always did. Well, I remember that me and my pal were occupied with some toy or other of his, in a corner of the room, when my disabled neighbour called us over.

We got up to walk across and it was at that moment that we noticed he was sat with his flies undone and he had this fat, hairy cock poking out. He was just sat there not saying anything and we didn't say anything either. I mean what the fuck *do* you say to some disabled guy who's just sat there with his penis out? I remember feeling a bit embarrassed and more than a bit fucking uncomfortable. We were both really young and so we didn't have a clue what the hell was going on.

I don't know to this day whether he was some kind of paedophile, or whether he was just sexually confused. Or maybe he had just cottoned onto the fact we were only there for his toys and thought he'd get his own back by getting his dick out. Whatever the reason, we sure as hell never went back to that house.

Chapter Four

It's not great growing up in a hairdressers shop, I can tell you. You probably think that it would be great; that you could have whatever hairstyle you wanted and enjoy a life without ever having to pay for your hair to be cut. The truth of the matter is, after standing up cutting every fucker's hair each day from eight in the morning to six in the evening, the last thing my dad could be arsed to do was bother with his kid's barnets.

That meant me and my sister were never the greatest advertisement for the shop and we always stuck out on the class photographs at school with our masses of unkempt hair. It's not like he did a great job whenever he *did* cut our hair. I remember this one time when I'd come home from school with a *beautiful* case of head lice. My dad sat me down in his shop, in this big chair in front of the mirror, and proceeded to cut almost *all* of my bleeding hair off. I grew up thinking that was the only way you could get rid of nits. I swear, it was only years later that I found out you could just buy lotions and stuff to treat them, rather than have to get scalped. I told you he was a real tight bastard.

My dad's mum had run the shop before him and she had set it up years and years ago with my granddad. My dad ran the Gent's side of the shop, and this was partitioned off from the Ladies' side which was run by my aunty. I was always a bit wary about walking into the Ladies' side of the shop and tried to avoid it whenever possible. I think it stemmed from when I was younger and the memories of pushing open the glass door and being hit by the pungent aroma of shampoos and hair dyes, and of smiling old women asking you to come and let them see how much you'd grown. They were only being nice and friendly but I'm not good in those kinds of situations – I never have been.

My dad and aunty had taken over the shop when my gran decided to move to Blackpool and set up a salon there. My granddad died before I was born so I never knew him, but he was a good sort, by all accounts. My grandma only died last year at the ripe old age of a hundred and two. It's weird how people are treated when they reach a hundred years old. Everyone acts like its some incredible achievement and I heard you're even supposed to get a telegram or something from the Queen. I suppose it reads a little like '*One Hundred Years Old! Stone me! I can't believe you're still alive!*' I mean, that's what people are pretty much thinking when they get told someone is a hundred. I always think that it must be quite stressful when you get to your sixties, seventies and beyond, knowing you might not even wake up in the morning. Fuck, I don't think I'd be able to even get to sleep just fretting about it.

Frankly – and again this is something that probably doesn't put me in a good light – I was pretty relieved when I heard she had finally died. It's not that I didn't like her or anything – she was really great. She was fairly tall for an old lady and rather thin and I always remember thinking she must have been quite pretty when she was younger. She had all this dark, wavy hair and it always looked good even though she was old – probably with her being a hairdresser. She lived in this grand house in Blackpool and we used to go and stay with her fairly regularly. She was awfully kind-hearted and usually busying around us whenever we went there. She'd spend ages in the kitchen making us these massive meals. It was wonderful gorging on food that hadn't been anywhere near a microwave for once. She'd present us each with huge plates steeped in food. It was delicious but I don't think my gran paid too much attention to sell-by dates 'cos on more than one occasion we'd have to stop the car on the return journey to Manchester to let me vomit all over the M61.

Everyone at school used to think me and my sister were incredibly lucky to have a gran that lived in Blackpool. I guess they thought that with her living in a seaside resort, we'd be able to visit the funfair and the arcades and the beach every time we went to see her. The stark reality was we probably got to see all that stuff even less than the kids at school. My dad used to say that he hated crowds of people and *that* was the reason he would rarely take us into the centre of Blackpool. I think it was probably *more* to do with the fact he'd have to spend some of his hard earned cash. Whenever he did take us, we'd never go to the main Pleasure Beach funfair and would usually just spend our time either on the beach or trawling around the piers. I didn't mind that though 'cos I really liked the arcades. It's quite an exciting experience walking around those arcades as a kid and seeing all the flashing lights and bleeping noises from the machines. We didn't usually have any money but I still liked watching other people on the video game machines and pinball tables. Occasionally, he'd give us some spare one and two pence pieces to use on the hypnotic, futile experience that is 'the penny falls'. It must be the only gambling machine in history where everybody that uses it is determined to end up losing.

They used to have this *Dr Who* exhibition in the centre of Blackpool. I was a big *Dr Who* fan as a little kid, although I haven't watched it since Tom Baker horrifically transformed into Peter Davidson. Whenever we went to see my gran, I'd always pester my dad to take me into town for the *Dr Who* exhibition. He knew I really loved that TV programme and so occasionally he'd take me along as a special treat. The entrance was via a replica blue T.A.R.D.I.S. spaceship, where you'd hand over the fee to some bored looking youth. Once inside, it was quite dark and there were loads of different *Dr Who* themed exhibits. You could stroll around the displays at your leisure, many of which comprised large replicas of the various alien adversaries of the Doctor. The problem was, it was quite a scary environment for a little kid and my dad would usually send me in on my own. He begrudged paying for me and so had absolutely *no* intention of paying for an adult ticket as well. Each time I visited, I'd be determined to make the most of my time there, but *every* time I'd be so filled with terror that I'd end up running straight through the entire exhibition. I'd stand in the safety of the bright lights in the gift shop at the exit trying to catch my breath and cursing my cowardice yet again. My disappointment would occasionally be somewhat tempered by my dad getting me something from the shop. Strategically avoiding the pricier toys and models, he'd usher me over to the stationery and we'd head back to the beach with me clutching my new *Doctor Who* – embossed pencil or eraser.

My gran was incredibly independent and pretty stubborn with it. I can remember when she started showing the first signs of dementia – for example she'd forget about leaving pans and stuff on the hob and then the pans would burn and get holes in them. It became quite apparent that it was too dangerous for her to live on her own and we all wanted her to leave her house and come and stay at my aunty's place, which was a large flat above the hairdressing shop. She was stubborn as hell though and was determined to stay in that house and keep her independence. My dad is *exactly* the same and I reckon I'll have the same kind of problems in a few years time. I can't fucking wait.

We finally got my gran to move to my aunty's flat above the shop and she stayed there for a year or so before she quickly deteriorated with the dementia. We ended up having to get her in an old people's home, so that she could have proper full time care. Even though she was going loopy, she still fought like mad about going in that care home. The last time that I saw her was for about five minutes one evening while she was still living with my aunty. My dad had finished work and I had been hanging around the shop. She'd not been living with my aunty for long and I felt really uncomfortable because I knew everyone expected me to go up and see her, but I really didn't want to. What I'm trying to say is that I *did* want to see her, but just not in the state I knew she was in. I mean, I don't like talking to people and exchanging niceties at the best of times, and I sure as hell don't like the awkwardness of talking to someone who hasn't got much of a clue about what the hell is going on.

Anyway, I climbed the stairs to my aunty's house that evening and knocked on the door before letting myself in. It was nice seeing my gran again and momentarily I felt a bit of a bastard for not wanting to come up and visit her. My aunty prompted my gran to look up to acknowledge that there was somebody there to see her. I remember she looked at me with her big brown eyes and a smile broke out across her wizened face before she spoke. She talked to me quite loudly, but I think that's 'cos she was also pretty deaf at that stage.

"Hello Stephen. Ooh, hasn't he grown?"

Now, the one thing you need to know at this stage of the story is that my name is *not* fucking Stephen. I felt it probably best not to point out her error, in case it upset and confused her even more, although my aunty was trying to explain the situation to her. That's the fucking cruellest thing about dementia – the sufferers for the most part don't completely lose their marbles, they just get confused really easily. They retain a semblance of mental stability; not enough that they can remember anything useful, but just enough to make them aware that they've been doing all kinds of nutty stuff. Anyhow, I only stayed up there about five minutes or so, although I swear it felt like five hours. I was mad that I'd felt pressured to go up there and that my memory of her would now be sullied 'cos I wouldn't be remembering her as this bright, independent woman anymore.

I never went to see her when they put her in that care home and I felt pretty bad about that, but I really didn't want to see her in that state. I used to get over the guilt of not seeing her by making myself not think about her at all. That sounds quite callous when I say it out loud but it's how I coped. My dad and aunty took turns going to see her everyday and you could tell my dad hated going and seeing her deteriorate, but I guess he felt like he had to go. So yeah, I was pretty relieved when she died and it meant my dad wouldn't have all that stress anymore.

We had her funeral at this little crematorium in Blackley in North Manchester. I don't know if my gran had specifically requested a cremation over a burial but I wouldn't put it past my dad to have just chosen the cheaper option. There were quite a lot of friends and relatives there, and some of my gran's old customers. There were even four or five women from the care home, which most people thought was nice, although I thought they'd probably just wanted the afternoon off work or something. Two of them seemed pretty upset though, so I guess I might have been wrong. I suppose if they went to the funeral of every old fucker they cared for then they'd only be in work about twelve days of the year. To be honest, they made me look a bit of a bastard 'cos I wasn't crying or snivelling and there they were, weeping away and they weren't even relatives or anything. I suppose it was quite nice that they were there and it said a lot for how lovely my gran was, even in her senile state.

Typically, my sister was late and missed the *whole* fucking service. I ended up sat with my two half brothers, about three rows from the front. They're both a few years older than me and the result of my dad's previous relationship before he got together with my mum. Don't ask me about it though 'cos I don't really know what happened and how he ended up with my mum and not theirs. I think he might have walked out on her and, if that's the case, I don't really wanna know. I'm not close to my half brothers at all but I really don't mind being related to them. They're both good guys.

I felt a little bit sad about my gran but, let's face it, she was *a hundred and fucking two* when she died. All that was going through my mind was that she'd had a fucking good innings. I'd have loved it if the woman from the crematorium had stood up at the front and kicked off with "Well, she had a fucking good innings", but she didn't.

Since my mum died *in her fucking forties*, I find it pretty difficult to be upset about anyone who dies, especially if they've had a relatively long life. I remember a couple of years back when a friend of mine was telling me about his granddad dying. He was visibly upset and I said I was sorry and everything, and I put on my best sad face and shook my head, but to be honest, I wasn't the least bit sorry. I mean he was in his fucking nineties, so it can't have been that much of a big bleeding surprise. That probably sounds a bit cold, but when you've had someone die on you way before they should have, you can't help but feel a little resentful.

Looking about that hall at my gran's service, I could see my dad was pretty cut up and my aunty was crying really hard so that all this snot was streaming from her nostrils. I suppose it's pretty difficult to look good when you're sobbing away like that but I still wished someone would have offered her a tissue. My cousins were both crying too and it made me concentrate even harder on looking really solemn. It wasn't anywhere near as tough as my mum's funeral though.

My sister cried loads throughout the entire day of my mum's funeral, but I swear I didn't cry one tear the whole time. I'm not trying to make out I'm some real hard bastard that never cries or anything, cos that couldn't be further from the truth. If anything, I'm *too* fucking emotional and I get upset at loads of stuff. I guess at my mum's funeral it all just seemed a bit surreal, like it was a bad dream or something. I mean, I knew she was dead and I knew she was in that coffin – trust me when we tried to carry it I fucking knew *something* was in that coffin – but I don't think I could properly grasp that it was all actually happening. And 'cos I didn't properly accept it, then I couldn't genuinely get upset and cry or anything.

Denial was probably the best state to be in 'cos death is one fact of life that's psychologically incredibly difficult to handle. It's maybe one of the only things that happen during a lifetime that you can't do one single fucking thing about. When other bad things happen you can usually comfort people by telling them not to worry and that things will get better. When someone dies, it's a situation that's *never* going to get better and so there's not much you can say to the bereaved. Nothing that will make them feel that much better, anyway.

I remember everyone kept coming up to me and my sister at my mum's funeral, saying how sorry they were and that she was a lovely woman and that they were really shocked et cetera, et cetera. Even though they were saying all those things it didn't make it seem any more real and, quite frankly, I just felt uncomfortable knowing that all that attention was on us. The crazy thing is, at one stage, I remember *pretending* to be crying, 'cos I was so paranoid that everyone would have been expecting it and wondering why I wasn't showing any emotion. I felt like shit, if you really want to know, thinking about how I was having to pretend to cry at my own mother's funeral.

Anyway, my gran's funeral went as well as you can expect these things to go. It wasn't a religious ceremony or anything, 'cos my gran wasn't interested in any of that rubbish, and so we didn't have to put up with a load of hymns and nonsensical babble and just stuck to talking about my gran. I always find it completely crazy during a lot of religious funerals when you get some representative from the church spouting on, when they know absolutely fuck all about the poor bleeder whose funeral it is. We had this priest who started proceedings off at my mum's funeral with the words 'Now, I didn't actually know Lynn.' *I mean – what the hell?* Why get someone to speak at the funeral of somebody they've never even fucking met? They then usually quote a load of confusing crap from the Bible that generally just brings everyone even further down. If you're gonna get someone to speak at a funeral that doesn't even fucking *know* the deceased, then at least get a fucking comedian, or ventriloquist, or someone with a bit more uplifting fucking material.

My dad got up in front of everyone at my gran's funeral and spoke for a while and it was pretty moving, to be honest. He cracked a lame gag about the doors being locked so that we'd all have to sit and listen, but it really was an interesting and emotional speech. On the downside, it did set my bleeding aunty off again, who'd only just stopped wailing. That speech made the day though and I felt really proud of him. At that moment in time, I was awfully glad that he was my dad.

Things took a turn for the worse though when one of my cousin's hideous children got up and rambled through some poem I'd never heard of. I think it was supposed be a touching moment where one of the latest generation reads out a really poignant, moving poem but it just made me feel like puking all over the row in front of us. They finished with some awful pop ballad, played on the crematorium's stereo system, and we all just had to sit there and endure it. I think it was supposed to be one of my gran's favourite songs, although if it was, it must have been when she had gotten really fucking senile. Overall though, it was pretty bearable and was all done and dusted in an hour or so. Man, some funerals go on for so long you feel like climbing in the bleeding coffin yourself by the time they've finished.

The absolute worst thing about funerals – even worse than the fact that some poor fucker has died – is the fact you have to attend the reception afterwards. Why do people have these bleeding receptions anyway? I can't actually think of a more *unsuitable* occasion to have a party. On this occasion, my dad had arranged for family and 'friends' to head back to his house after the funeral for a drink and a bite to eat.

I really hate those types of forced gatherings where you're stuck in a room with people you have nothing in common with. I mean it's not so bad being around your close family, although that is bad enough, but at these types of things you're stuck with their extended family too. I'm really no good at all at making small talk and feigning interest at people's responses. My eyes glaze over and I get all panicky and feel like I just wanna run out of the room screaming. I swear, sometimes I start to speak to people and my voice pretty much trails off before I've even finished, 'cos I get so fucking bored with what I'm saying. I try and desperately avoid eye contact with people in the hope that will make me immune from their inane conversation. I really would much rather sit in silence with my own thoughts than pretend I'm the *slightest* bit interested in what job somebody does or what they're having done to their fucking kitchen. Sometimes people misinterpret this aversion to mundane chatter as me being an ignorant bastard. I do try though, I really do, but after a while of trying to look like I'm even remotely interested, I can feel my face start to give the game away. It's a fucking curse, I swear.

I remember that particular day we were all in this cramped back room at my dad's house. My stepsister kept walking back and forth from the kitchen with plates of cheap, cold pizza, sausage rolls and other assorted delights. The Ambassador's reception, it fucking *wasn't*. My step mum has always been an incredibly awful cook and any invitations for dinner

44

are avoided like the plague by the rest of the family. It's no wonder me and my sister were really skinny throughout our school days, when we were totally reliant on her cooking every evening to provide us with the required nutritional intake. Her cuisine was dreadful, but it was made even worse by the fact she used to cook meals the previous day, or at best, in the morning, and then reheat in the evening ready to serve up her speciality: a plate of barely edible, congealed crap. The invention of the microwave might have been a technological breakthrough that was lauded by the rest of the civilised world, but in one terraced house in North Manchester it was rued almost every fucking day.

She was always insistent that we cleared our plate which was some bleeding mission I can tell you, since every mouthful would usually result in involuntary retching from within. It wasn't just that the cooking was bad, she'd also serve up stuff that she knew very fucking well we didn't even like.

"I know you don't like sprouts, so I've just given you a few."

We could never understand how she struggled with the concept of us not actually liking some foodstuffs. She believed that if you didn't like it, then it just meant you didn't want as much of it on your plate as stuff that you *did* like.

Given that the food was inedible, and that we'd be in the shit if we didn't clear our plates, each evening involved me and my sister concocting plans on the scale of the most ingenious military operations. The main problem we had was that the dining table was against a side wall in the same room where she'd sit slovenly glued to the TV set each evening. We'd have to wait until she either went to the toilet, or pick a moment that we thought she was sufficiently engrossed in *Crossroads* not to notice us. We'd then take the opportunity to head into the kitchen along with our plates still filled with congealed muck and the addition of our tears and vomit. If she wasn't immersed enough in her programme, her head would swivel round and she'd glare and ask where we were going. We'd have to sit down again and wait for the next available opportunity. Once we did manage to get past her we'd race to the dustbin in the kitchen and fight to be the first to scrape the contents into the bin and camouflage it with other rubbish, in order to cover our tracks. Occasionally we'd almost be thwarted by the bin being empty and so we'd hastily blow our noses on tissue paper or scan the kitchen for other things to cover up the microwaved crap.

I remember the time we found out that we were getting a dog. Me and my sister were ecstatic, not so much at the thought of having a pet, but more at the instant realisation that we'd be able to offload all future meals under the table to that dog. Now it's a well known fact that dogs will fucking eat *anything*. Well, that's what we had thought until the first day we discovered that they'll eat anything *bar her cooking*. I recall our first attempt and the difficulty we had explaining why the cheese flan we'd been dished up for tea was all over the carpet underneath the dining table.

Anyway, my sister finally turned up half an hour

into the reception following my gran's funeral. She was all full of tears and self pity about how she'd missed the funeral but nobody had been in the least bit fucking surprised. My dad wasn't even the slightest bit bothered – though you can bet your life if *I'd* been the one to miss that funeral he'd have bollocked me and moaned about it for months. I swear if my sister had fucking *killed* my gran she'd still have gotten away scot free.

Chapter Five

Looking at my step mum now you wouldn't believe for a minute she was anything other than a harmless, gentle old soul. To be honest, she *is* pretty much harmless now. She's practically house bound and has all kinds of medical problems. She needs a wheelchair when she does go out anywhere and she uses a stick to help her get about the house. She's only in her sixties but I swear it takes her about half a fucking hour to get out of the armchair she spends the majority of her life in. I feel a bit sorry for her to tell you the truth, although I shouldn't have an ounce of pity for her, considering the way she used to treat us when we were kids. I don't quite know how my dad ended up with her but, if you ask me, I think it was just circumstance more than anything.

My memories are pretty hazy but it seemed like my mum and dad split up and almost instantly she appeared. My mum had gotten quite bad with the depression and all and couldn't look after me and my sister, so we had to live with my dad after the split. As I said, I'm not too clear on the events and I think it's probably 'cos if I think about it rationally then it seems like my dad left my mum when she was in a bit of a mess and needed his support. That doesn't make me feel too good, so I'm not gonna dwell on it. All I know is that all of a sudden we had to move away and my mum wasn't around anymore. And *she* was in my mum's place.

I say circumstance was the driver between my dad and my step mum getting together as she had just split up from her husband and I think my dad would have welcomed any offer at that time, being that he had his hands full looking after us and working full time. My dad was quite a hard working guy, unlike me. He'd toil long hours, stood up all day in the shop cutting hair and then he'd often work Friday and Saturday nights in a band. And before you start, that's nowhere near as bleeding exciting as you might think it is. Ever since he was a young guy, he and a few pals would play together in this band at various functions around Manchester. They'd play in hotels mostly and would set up in the corner and play a load of middle-of-the-road tunes to a load of middle-of-the-road people. You know the type of band I mean 'cos you've probably seen them at weddings or birthday parties or some other awful fucking celebratory event. They largely just play anonymously in the corner and are generally ignored until people start getting drunk and begin dancing like twats. He really enjoyed playing in that band though, despite it being a pretty tough schedule working in the shop all day and then having to go and play till the early hours of the morning. They still played the odd function together, up until quite recently, but unfortunately for their legions of fans, the group had to split up after three of them died of old age. *Rock and fucking roll.*

Once my dad had left my mum, we stayed in the living quarters at the back of the shop for a while. Then, when he got together with my step mum, we moved to that maisonette in Ardwick I told you about. We weren't there that long really before they bought this terraced house together in Moston, another dreadful part of Manchester. My sister had to share a room with my step sister and, to be fair; she was the least awful member of their family. There was at least an air of normality about her that was missing in spades from the rest of her clan. She had jet black hair and wasn't that bad looking, in truth, although I was always put off by the fact that one day she'd probably end up looking like my step mum. That and the fact I thought it might be illegal to get it on with your step sister. *Is it?* I still don't know to this day, although looking at her now I'm pretty fucking glad I never really gave it a second thought.

Both of her brothers were complete fuckwits. The eldest brother had his own room and was kinda creepy, if you must know. He had these goofy teeth, lank, mousy, greasy hair and awful National Health glasses. I think I'm making him sound handsomer than he was, to be honest. It was bad enough that I was associated with him by living in the same house, but one day he managed to alienate us even further from all the local kids. You won't even believe what I'm gonna tell you but, I swear to God, it's fucking true.

As well as being incredibly ugly, the eldest brother was also what you might describe as 'a fucking weirdo'. He didn't work, and he spent most of his days in his room; masturbating and attempting to contact like-minded dickheads on this CB radio that he had. He was also a bit of a low-rent, Walter Mitty type character. He used to invent all kinds of stories that you just knew were absolute crap. There was this one time when he started to tell us about Captain X.

Apparently, my step brother wasn't just the repulsive, socially-inadequate loser we all thought he was. He was also a super hero. A super hero by the name of Captain X. When a grown man in his early twenties tells you he has a super hero alter ego named Captain X, the normal response is to cringe and get the fuck away as fast as possible. Unfortunately, we lived with the cunt and so we just had to ignore him and hope he never uttered the tale to anybody outside of our home.

One Sunday afternoon, I'd gone to the nearby woods to walk the dog. My sister had come too, along with my step sister and one of her friends. I remember it was autumn time and there were leaves everywhere. We were messing around, running after the dog and getting that buzz you do as a kid when you start kicking leaves about and hear them crunching underfoot. All of a sudden, the dog started barking towards a clearing, up ahead, and we all looked up to see a figure emerge from the trees. It was a man dressed in a white t-shirt and red shorts, with a black, balaclava mask covering his face. We were close enough to make out the words that were scrawled in black felt tip across his t-shirt: CAPTAIN X. He didn't say a word and we all just stood there, staring at him nonplussed. Seconds later, he vanished again, running off behind the trees. Even the fucking dog couldn't believe what it had just witnessed. The shittest super hero in the entire world.

We confronted him after we'd got back, but he denied all knowledge of it. It wouldn't have been so bad if it was just us that had seen him, but my step sister's friend had been there and she quite unhelpfully told every bleeding kid in the neighbourhood. Quite rightly, he got labelled by the whole community as the local nut job but we got tarred with the same brush by association. It was a rough area and his antics meant it wasn't safe for me to leave the house and none of the local kids ever wanted to be friends with us. Thankfully, we never saw Captain X again. If *you're* ever in trouble, I wouldn't recommend getting your hopes up if that particular super hero turns up at the scene. He'd probably just rape your kids and disappear.

One positive thing I will say for my step brother though, was that he unwittingly supplied me with a raft of porn magazines throughout my teenage years. He was obviously a seasoned pervert and his stash of high brow literature was extremely welcome in an age where the average teenager had to rely on page three of *The Sun* or the lingerie section of the Kays catalogue for their carnal entertainment.

Things are obviously different these days 'cos everybody has the internet and the world of pornography is just a mouse click away. Fuck, if I was a teenager today I don't think I'd ever wanna leave my bedroom. It does kind of skew your image of women though, when you spend the majority of your adolescence leafing through the likes of *Escort* and *Mayfair*. It was only years later I'd discover that women in the real world don't wear full make up and dress in stockings and suspenders every single night and there wasn't the merest fucking suggestion of underarm hair or panty liners in *Razzle*. I always remember when I used to look at those magazines that the reality of getting a *real* woman to take her clothes off in front of me seemed a fucking world away. And if it did happen, I always believed that I'd probably ejaculate the second her bra came off. Come to think of it, I wasn't far fucking wrong the first few times.

The eldest brother used to keep loads of these magazines under his bed and although he let me borrow them occasionally, he always made me hand them back over. Those magazines were pretty tame really, but to a horny thirteen year old it was like being given the keys to Blackbeard's bleeding treasure. They were full of pictures of naked women in suggestive poses, alongside supposed letters from readers eager to put into writing how they'd just been going about their business and had ended up having sex with their gorgeous wife's sister, or their mate's nymphomaniac wife, or some Swedish triplets that had just happened to pass by. When I read those letters, it felt like everybody was getting it, bar me.

I remember one time, my step brother was out of the house and I was in my room feeling a bit frisky, so I thought I'd go and help myself to one of the magazines from under his mattress. My room was at the front of the house, next to my sister's room, and so I had to creep along the landing past my dad's room and then past the bathroom until I got to his room at the back of the house. My step mum and sister were downstairs and I could hear the TV blaring out from the lounge. I stood outside his bedroom door and called his name. I knew he was out but I guess I was just being extra careful. I gently pressed the handle down and slowly pushed his door open.

There, in front of me, was his mangy bed with only a grotty mattress between me and my prize. I immediately knew how Indiana Jones must have felt in the opening of *Raiders of the Lost Ark* when he manoeuvres past all the dangerous pitfalls before feasting his eyes on the solid gold idol. Although Indiana Jones only had to avoid deadly traps and plot his way past thousands of huge spiders and rats in that film. I bet you there's no way he would have been brave enough to venture past that filthy fucking mattress. I closed my eyes and slowly eased my hand underneath the stain-ridden bedding and grabbed hold of a magazine. All of a sudden, I could hear the TV downstairs getting louder and I knew the lounge door had been opened. I froze on the spot. My step mum called out as she must have spotted his bedroom door was open.

"Neil, are you in Stephen's room?"

I panicked and didn't know what to say. So I didn't say anything. I hoped she would just carry on into the kitchen. But she didn't. I heard the creaking of the stairs as she began to make her way up the steps.

"Neil?"

I shoved the magazine back under the mattress, bolted out of the room and waltzed straight past her as she walked up the stairs. I knew I had to say something though.

"Er, yeah. I was just looking out of the window."

As excuses go, it was fucking abysmal. It wasn't even as if there *was* anything to look at. His room looked out onto our concrete flagged back yard, and then onto the concrete flagged back yard of the neighbour from across the way. As views go, let's just say it wasn't the Hanging fucking Gardens of Babylon. I heard her go in his room for a few seconds and then she closed his door and went back downstairs. Fuck knows what she thought I was doing. I didn't feel much like trying again after she'd gone. Besides, she'd killed the moment.

That reminds me of another time though, when I got embarrassed by my real mum a couple of years later over the same kind of thing. Me and my sister would usually stay at her house at the weekends and would return on the Sunday night. It was always really depressing waiting for my dad to turn up on the Sunday evening, knowing we'd have to leave my mum and return to that horrible house in Moston with my ghastly step family. Our misery was compounded by the thought of having to go to school the following day.

One Sunday, when we'd not long left my mum's house and returned back to my dad's house, he shouted up the stairs that my mum was on the phone. I casually jogged downstairs and grabbed the receiver off my dad. The phone in that house used to be attached to the middle of the white, woodchip papered wall in the lounge where the television was. Anytime anybody rang, my step mum would turn the TV volume right down for the *entire* duration of the call. It basically meant that it was a fucking waste of time *anybody* ever ringing you 'cos as soon as you'd start talking she'd turn the sound off. Not only would you be conscious that they were all listening to every word you said, but she also made you feel that they couldn't continue watching TV until you'd finished.

Anyway, I grabbed the receiver that time and heard my mum on the other end of the line.

"Hi Neil."

"Hi Mum."

"Is that your magazine under your duvet on your bed?"

Oh fuck. It suddenly flashed across my mind that I'd forgotten to hide a porn magazine that I'd been looking at. I'd sneaked one of my stepbrother's magazines out of the house 'cos I knew he wouldn't miss one from the stacks of publications he'd amassed. And even if he did, I knew he'd never enquire over breakfast as to whether anybody had seen a missing copy of *Color Climax*. I usually hid it under my mattress (I learnt from the Master) but I realised I couldn't remember returning it to its hiding place. I remember I didn't know what to say and felt my cheeks burn up to a ridiculously scarlet hue. I mean, I couldn't really deny knowledge of its existence and I couldn't think of anybody else I could blame. I usually blamed my sister for everything but I didn't think I'd be able to pin this one on her. It was under *my* duvet on *my* bed. My mum didn't exactly have to be fucking Columbo to work out who it belonged to.

"Er, yeah. It's mine."

"OK. I was just checking."

"OK. Bye mum."

"Bye."

What was the fucking point of that call? She must have

known it was mine and she must have known that call would have been *really* embarrassing for me. Some of the pictures and stories in that magazine kept flashing through my mind and I started to feel really nauseous knowing my mum had been looking at them. I kept wondering if I'd left it open at a particular page.

If you ask me, it's crazy in this day and age the way that you're thought of as some kind of pervert if you look at porn. I mean, it's a natural instinct to want sex and I can't for the life of me see how it's perverted to want to see images of the opposite sex naked. Frankly, I think you're fucking perverted if you *don't*.

"What did your mum want?"

Fuck.

"Nothing. She just wanted to speak to me."

I ran upstairs, fully aware that my face was still beaming red. I knew, right then, that I really had to start thinking a bit quicker on my feet. I'm piss poor at lying – I always have been. The thing is, lying is such an important facet of everyday life. You have to be able to lie if you want to get by in society. For example, when somebody asks whether you like their new haircut or a new jacket or something, the only answer you can give them is 'yes'. The crazy thing is, even if that hairstyle or jacket makes them look fucking appalling, you have to say it looks good so as not to hurt their feelings. In my mind it would be more helpful to be honest and tell them they look a right twat and that they need to change their hair back or return that jacket to the shop.

Don't get me wrong, I'm a coward so I'll always tell

people what they want to hear, but my face is never really convincing when I'm doing it. It's like when someone tells a joke that isn't funny and the polite response is to fake a laugh. Some people go overboard and laugh really loudly like they've just heard the funniest thing ever. I try and fake a laugh but it always comes out really forced and unconvincing. I start to stress when someone even *starts* to tell me a joke 'cos I panic about coming up with a convincing laugh. I definitely worry about these things too much.

I shared a room with the younger step brother for a short time. He wasn't quite as ugly as his brother and that's about the best thing I can say about him. I came back home from school one day to find that he'd fucked off to Scotland and had taken most of my stuff with him. I could have understood him stealing food or money to take on his journey but fuck knows what he planned to do with things like my record collection and my soap-on-a-rope. Apparently, his dad had moved north of the border and my step mum got a call a few days later to say that's where he was. I was really happy he'd fucked off but, as you can imagine, I was less than bleeding happy he'd taken my stuff with him.

My dad told me not to worry and said that if I made a list, he'd replace everything that had been taken. Like a fucking idiot, I actually believed he would fork out for it all and I remember painstakingly writing a long list split into separate sub-sections.

Vinyl – 7 inch

Kids in America – Kim Wilde.

Road to Nowhere – Talking Heads.

Boxerbeat – JoBoxers.

Reward – Teardrop Explodes.

We All Stand Together – Paul McCartney & The Frog Chorus.

Pretty eclectic fucking mix, eh? I didn't even try and scam my dad by putting on stuff I wanted but hadn't had, although, like I say, it was a fucking waste of time anyway 'cos he didn't replace *any* of my stuff. There was more chance of Paul McCartney and his fucking Frog Chorus turning up in my bedroom and singing that song to me, than there was my dad forking out the cash for that seven inch record.

Anyhow, the fact that cunt had scarpered ensured I didn't have to share my room anymore and I had somewhere to retreat to every evening. Believe you me, in that fucking house I *really* needed somewhere to escape to.

Chapter Six

My dad got married to my step mum not long after we'd moved to that house. I guess she must have got divorced from that bald fucker she was married to, and my dad didn't have to worry 'cos he was never married to my mum. Growing up, I didn't know anybody else whose parents weren't married and I never used to publicise the fact that mine weren't, especially when I found out it meant that me and my sister were, quite literally, bastards. Not a great fucking title to have, I can tell you.

Before my dad married my step mum, he sat me and my sister down and said he wanted our consent. He explained that if we weren't happy about it then he wouldn't marry her. My sister just said straight away that she *was* happy with it, but she's one of those people that never think anything through and probably put more thought into buying a pair of shoes than into having a baby. I, on the other hand, fucking analyse *everything*, which inevitably leads to bleeding misery and heartache. Don't get me wrong, I told him I was happy for him to marry her, but I sure as fuck didn't mean it. To be honest, I wasn't particularly bothered about him marrying her for all the difference it would make. I guess I just felt like I was kind of betraying my mum and siding with the enemy. My mum wasn't too fond of her, to put it politely, and I thought the news would probably upset her. It was obviously what my dad wanted though, so my only options were to either say no and upset my dad, or give my blessing and upset my mum. As you can imagine, it wasn't exactly a great fucking decision to have to make. It was bleeding uncomfortable sat slap bang between that rock and a hard place.

We didn't have to go to the wedding, thankfully, as they just had it at a registry office one day when we were at school. I saw the photos and they were pretty fucking gruesome, which was to be expected. My dad hadn't exactly gone to town and was dressed in this ill-fitting brown suit that he'd probably had since the war. His trousers were at half-mast in an unconscious symbol of mourning at the act of union that had just taken place. She had this cheap dark blue outfit on and this stupid hat with a veil that, to everyone's disappointment, only partially covered her face. As you've probably noticed by now, I haven't got the broadest vocabulary in the world, but I swear there aren't words to describe how ugly she is. I was genuinely embarrassed being seen out with her for fear of people thinking she was something to do with me. I'm probably sounding a bit harsh about her, and you're probably feeling a bit sorry for her, but my attitude towards her wasn't down to the way she looked – although that was reason enough – it was more to do with the way she treated us.

I've probably painted a picture of my dad so far as some mean disciplinarian. Don't get me wrong, he is stingy with his cash and he is strict on discipline, but he's also pretty fucking great. He's immensely talented and can play a whole host of musical instruments. He writes his own songs, he seems to be able to fix pretty much anything; fuck, without a word of a lie, he even built his own boat from scratch! He seems to excel at everything he turns his hand too. I remember he wrote this great poem once that was published in the *Manchester Evening News*. It was called something like 'Man's Inhumanity to Man.' It was about how soldiers returning from the war were shoddily treated by society and pretty much forgotten about. Now I'm no expert on poetry, but I reckon it was pretty fantastic work for a hairdresser from North Manchester to come up with.

He still surprises me even now with how talented he is – his speech at my gran's funeral that I told you about was pretty much perfect. I wish I could do an ounce of the things he can. I swear I can't even change a bleeding plug. He's not just talented though, he's a good dad too, all things considered. He always made sure me and my sister knew how much he loved us and he would try and take time out after work to give us hugs and affection. That all changed though when he got together with my step mum. I think it used to bug her that she never had the same kind of relationship with her kids. It wouldn't surprise me if she'd never once told those poor fuckers that she loved them.

What usually happened was that she'd start picking fights with my dad whenever he'd spend time, or be affectionate, with us. I don't know what her fucking problem was; whether she was just jealous of him giving attention to anyone but her, whether she just despised us for being his link to my mum, or whether she just hated the fact she didn't have the same bond with her litter of degenerates. Whatever it was, she used to always make his life difficult and make it pretty fucking clear that she thought it was pathetic if he'd play games or be affectionate towards us.

We often used to hear them rowing like crazy when we were upstairs in bed. I hate arguing and bad feeling and it used to give me this sick feeling in my stomach. I used to pull the sheets over my head and try and drown the shouting out. I thought that if I couldn't hear them arguing, then I could just pretend it wasn't happening. It never really worked though. The way she argued with my dad was the real reason me and my sister used to despise her. She just seemed full of hate and we didn't so much mind her being horrible to us, but we couldn't help but resent her for constantly upsetting my dad. He did seem to act a little bit differently towards us after a while though and would usually just be like his old self on the odd occasion she wasn't around. I guess he probably thought it wasn't worth all the earache. He was probably right.

Every evening at bedtime, me and my sister would get our pyjamas on, before going to the bathroom to brush our teeth and wash. My dad would always come into our bedrooms and tuck us in and say 'good night', but before that we'd usually have to traipse downstairs to say 'good night' to *her*. It would always be difficult enough to summon up the energy to wish her a 'good night' that wasn't *totally* devoid of all sincerity, but that was nothing compared to the effort it required for us to pucker up and kiss her on the cheek each night. One particular night, at bedtime, I said something that I immediately regretted, and that I've regretted saying ever since.

You see, I think my dad realised how much we disliked my step mum and he really wanted us to try and be more accepting of her. We didn't ever tell him we despised her, but it was pretty fucking obvious that we weren't happy that she and her family had been forced upon us. We tried our best to go along with it though, 'cos we knew it's what my dad wanted. I think he was eager to try and appease her as much as possible and I imagine he thought she might mellow a little around the house if we showed her more affection.

He had tentatively broached the subject of us calling her 'mum' a couple of times, but we just dismissed it out of hand. I dunno if she'd complained that we didn't call her mum but it was typically the kind of unreasonable request that she *would* make. We usually only called her by her first name, but that particular night I walked up to her in my pyjamas and said 'good night, mum'. I think they'd been arguing a lot and I thought it might help make things easier for my dad if I went along with things and pretended I was comfortable affording her that title. It didn't change anything though, and I never called her by that name again. I felt bad as soon as I'd uttered it and I wanted to phone my mum up straight away and apologise. I'd not really thought about that night again for a long time but it came into my mind the day I left the hospital after my mum had died. I really like tormenting myself for some reason.

I always remember dreading parent's evenings at school – not because I struggled academically – but because I didn't want other kids and teachers seeing her and assuming it was my mum. Come to think of it, I can't ever recall my real mum ever being at a parent's evening. She didn't live near my school for most of my education and she didn't drive, so I guess it would have been difficult for her to get there. I'm probably just making excuses for her though 'cos I suppose she didn't really ever seem that interested in our schooling. My mum was in hospital a lot of the time we were at school anyway.

I told you before that she suffered with depression and I think that's why she ended up in Prestwich Hospital. If you don't know it, it's this place in North Manchester and it's not like a regular hospital. It's what you'd probably call a 'nuthouse' or 'mental hospital'. It was well known in Manchester and all the kids at school knew it as some kind of 'loony bin', so me and my sister never mentioned that Mum was there. Kids can be pretty fucking cruel and I'm sure they would have had a field day if they'd have found out. When kids in the playground would say the nasty things that kids do, you'd occasionally hear them call each other mental and say they were gonna get sent to Prestwich Hospital. I was pretty sure a sympathetic arm around the shoulder and a few consoling words would have been the last things we'd have got from those little fuckers.

When she was in that hospital, my dad used to take us to visit her during the weekends. Sometimes she'd cancel at the last minute though, if she wasn't feeling too good and couldn't face up to seeing us. That was pretty disappointing 'cos we looked forward all week to seeing her, even in that place, and it's hard to understand when you're a kid why your mum wouldn't want to see you. It's difficult to quite comprehend what depression is though. I could never get why she couldn't just snap out of it and cheer up. When I was older, I remember getting mad with her a few times about it. I guess I was just frustrated 'cos I couldn't help, but it's another thing I don't exactly feel too good about now when I think back.

I still don't exactly know the reasons why she used to get depressed but I know she went downhill after the accident and I think she struggled with stuff from her childhood too. I didn't know too much about her mum and dad as we never met them. I knew they lived in Wales and I remember that my mum really didn't like her dad. She used to talk to my sister much more than to me, especially later in her life, and my sister once said that apparently he'd abused my mum in some way. I never wanted to hear any of that stuff so I just changed the subject when my sister mentioned it. I really can't cope thinking about stuff like that. Like with the arguing, if I don't listen to it and I don't think about it, then I can pretend it hasn't happened.

There was this girl I want to tell you about that I used to see when I was in my mid-twenties. I met her in some terrible club in town, one Saturday night. I'd been loitering near the dance floor and I'd noticed her 'cos she was really good-looking. I remember I didn't have to go through the rigmarole of chatting her up 'cos this guy had been getting a bit familiar with her and she had told him that she was with me, in order that he'd leave her alone. We got on pretty well and ended up having a bit of a kiss at the end of the evening. Like I said, she was really attractive and a lot more entertaining than most of the bores you end up getting landed with. She had this Spanish look about her, shoulder length chestnut brown hair, gorgeous green eyes and this smile that was pretty sexy. I didn't notice immediately, but she had great knockers as well, which is always a bonus. I remember thinking I'd struck gold as she seemed perfect in every way. It all seemed to be going well until I was brought crashing down to Earth.

"So, have you got a boyfriend?"

"No."

Perfect.

"I've got a husband."

Bollocks.

I told her my number at the end of the night but obviously I didn't put much hope in ever seeing her again. Anyway, it seems her marriage was on the rocks and about a week later she called me and asked to see me again. She ended up splitting up with him and we were together about three years – we even lived together for quite a while.

She still lived with her husband for the first few months I was seeing her. After a while, she was pretty open with him about the situation and she even used to ring me from the house and I could hear him milling about in the background. It was pretty fucking weird. When I first started seeing her though, it was behind his back and so it was all secretive, clandestine stuff. One time, I'd arranged to meet her in this awful bar in town about nine o' clock. I got there about twenty to nine 'cos I always like to get to places first when

I'm meeting someone. That way, I can grab a drink and relax and pick a good spot before they turn up. Anyhow, it turns out this bar was completely shut and so I had little alternative but to stand outside and wait for her to show. What I didn't realise though, was that her husband had insisted on giving her a lift into town. About five past nine, this car pulled up next to the bar, about a hundred yards from where I was stood.

It was completely dark inside the bar, and it was really quiet outside on the street, except for the odd person who'd occasionally walk by. It was a Monday night and there wasn't much going on. I started feeling real panicky 'cos I knew it must have looked pretty suspicious, what with me being the only person stood there outside a bar that was closed, with no sign of the friends she was supposed to have been meeting. I remember trying to think how someone would behave if they were waiting for somebody that *definitely* wasn't a passenger in that car.

Should I be looking at the car?

Should I not be looking at the car?

It wasn't exactly *Academy Award* winning acting, but I kept looking at my watch and glancing left and right down the street, whilst sighing in an exaggerated manner. They seemed to be just sat in that car forever and, just as I was about to start walking away, I heard the car door open and shut, and the engine start as he began to drive away. Although I was incredibly relieved, I felt pretty bad towards her husband, even though I didn't know him at all. It wasn't a great thing to do to someone, but I can't have felt that bad 'cos once I was certain that car wasn't coming back, then I was kissing her like mad and groping her like the dirty bastard I am. Looking back, it was pretty exciting stuff.

This other time when everything was out in the open, I went round to see her at her house. Her husband had gone out somewhere or other and so she had wanted to take advantage of having somewhere free for us to be together. I had only agreed to go on the proviso that he wouldn't be around. I told her it was because I didn't want to humiliate him, but the truth was I didn't fancy being on the receiving end of any violence. He was apparently okay with the situation but I didn't want to take any chances. The night wasn't that great in all honesty 'cos I couldn't relax with the knowledge that he might show up at any time.

I didn't drive in those days and I'd gotten to her house by taking a tram. Later on that evening, I left her house and ran to the tram stop to make the return journey home. My relief at leaving her house quickly turned to panic when I found out that I'd missed the last tram. I hadn't realised but apparently they stopped running earlier on Sundays. I didn't have a clue how else to get home and I knew my only option was to run back to her house and ask her to order me a taxi. I raced back and was overjoyed to find he hadn't returned, although I knew I'd still have to sweat on my taxi turning up promptly. I remember standing at her front door waiting for my ride home when a car pulled up and this guy got out and started walking towards her house. I automatically knew it was her husband and I began to mentally prepare myself for a punch on the nose. He was a bit of a big bastard, I can tell you.

Anyway, he opened the gate and came right up to me and said 'Alright, mate', whilst thrusting out his hand for me to shake. He pretty much almost broke my fucking hand when we shook and then he marched on into the house. I stopped shaking for a minute and practically ran towards the taxi when it finally turned up.

Anyway, the whole reason I told you about that girl was that I remember a couple of times, when we were living together, that she had gotten quite upset and had tried to talk to me about something that had happened to her when she was young. From the bits she told me it appears that a relative had molested her or something. I can't comprehend how anyone could do that to a kid, let alone a member of their own fucking family. Anyway, the thing is, I couldn't handle being told that stuff. When she was crying and beginning to tell me, I just got mad and told her I didn't want to hear it. That made her even more upset but, honestly, I just couldn't stand it. She must have been really upset about those memories and it took a lot of courage for her to tell me about it. She was looking to me to comfort her and make things better. I couldn't do it though and I really hate myself for it. I'm a fucking coward, I swear.

I really cared about that girl. I guess I still do. We split up though and, as usual, it was all my fault. I have a habit of messing up relationships I'm in and causing people loads of heartache. I swear it's not intentional though. It's just that, once I've been seeing somebody for quite a while, I start to question whether that relationship is 'the one'. Once I start getting the usual pressure to settle down properly and commit and make plans then I just get really panicky. I start worrying about committing in case I realise down the line that it's the wrong decision. At that stage, breaking up would hurt them even more and would be so much harder to do. I mean, how do you know what's the right decision to make? How do you know that things are gonna work out and that you're meant to be with that person? So what I do – and this is really fucked up – is that I end the relationship on the basis I'm not one hundred per cent sure that being with them is the right thing to do. My reasoning is that I'm not certain about things, so at least by ending it I'm allowing her to be able to move on and meet someone else and be happy. It's not like I think I don't love them anymore, 'cos I really do. It's just my twisted way of thinking things through. I'm really quite messed up.

Prestwich Hospital itself just seemed like a normal hospital inside, with these vast white rooms and sprawling corridors. I'd be excited about seeing my mum whenever we went there, but I'd also have this sort of uneasy feeling in my stomach. I think it's 'cos we got quite a bit of attention off the other residents when we arrived. There never seemed to be many other visitors there and we never saw any other children. There were loads of patients walking about and unfortunately they'd always start talking to us. I'm no good with that kind of thing at the best of times but these people were real fruitcakes and would often start talking gibberish to us or begin shouting loudly. It's difficult to know how to react in those situations, especially when you're a kid, and we usually just tended to get embarrassed and look away. We really couldn't understand why our mum was in there with all those mad people.

Whenever we'd see her she didn't look ill or anything. She wouldn't act as though she was different in any way. She just looked like our mum and I wanted her to leave that place so we could go stay with her at weekends again. Sometimes she'd have stints at home and seem happy and we'd think she was cured but then, during the week, my dad would receive a call that she was ill again and that she'd been admitted back into that place. It was quite upsetting to keep thinking you were gonna get your mum back, only for her to be taken away again. Looking back, all those bouts of depression must have resulted in her being classed as mentally unstable and that's why they kept her in that hospital so long. And, at that time, me and my sister didn't know anything about the suicide attempts.

Chapter Seven

I can't remember enjoying any of my time at school. I mean, I always enjoyed playing football during P.E., but that was about it. Academically, I'd always do just enough to get by, without particularly excelling in any of my classes. When my mum and dad split up, we were transferred to a primary school near where my dad worked. It made sense 'cos he was the one looking after me and my sister full time, so he had to be able to leave work and pick us up when we finished for the day. I didn't dislike primary school as much as secondary school, but it was still somewhere I really didn't wanna be. We'd only usually see my mum at weekends in those days and sometimes, like when she was in hospital, we might only see her for a couple of hours on a Sunday. Occasionally we wouldn't see anything of her for a few weeks.

It was upsetting not being able to see my mum that much in those days. I suppose it made us appreciate her more though when we did get to see her. I remember this one time, when she'd bought me a pack of that card game – Top Trumps. I was really chuffed with them. They had this horror theme and featured characters like Dracula, Frankenstein and The Wolfman. I remember the Dracula card was pretty much unbeatable and had really high scores across all the categories. I think he could only be beaten by Death on the 'Killing Power' category. I was obsessed about all things horror-related and so like I said, I really loved those cards. I would have liked those cards off anybody, but I liked them even more 'cos they were off my mum. It sounds really silly but 'cos I didn't get to see her that much, it felt good to always have something with me that she'd bought for me.

One day I'd been playing in the schoolyard at that primary school near my dad's shop. It was a pretty cold, blustery day and I'd been running round like crazy, as most kids tend to do when they get into wide, open spaces. All of a sudden, I stopped running for a second 'cos I heard a bit of commotion behind me. I turned to see a bunch of children chasing some objects that were swirling around in the breeze. The kids were shouting and running in circles, occasionally stooping to try and beat the others to retrieve something off the floor. I quickly realised what the objects of their desire were. The items that were fluttering about in the wind were Top Trumps cards. I knew immediately that they were mine, but I still reached into my back pocket to check. Sure enough the plastic case which had held them was gone. It must have fallen out whilst I'd been running and now the cards were being blown backwards and forwards across the playground. I felt sick to my stomach and I frantically began to grab as many of the remaining cards as possible. I could feel big tears rolling down my icy cheeks as I gathered what cards I could whilst uttering to those that would listen that the cards they'd salvaged were mine. The bell went to signal our return to the classroom and I remember tightly grasping the recovered few cards in my hands.

I was still crying uncontrollably. All I could think about was the fact my mum had bought those cards for me, even though she didn't have much money. And now I'd gone and lost them. That memory has stayed crystal clear with me all these years, so I guess it must have had a pretty big emotional impact on me as a kid.

I had this pal called Iain at that primary school. Apart from his name, I can't really remember anything else about him, except for the fact that he always had a packet of crisps at break time. I used to spend that whole break time in the playground hoping he'd share them with me. You were allowed to bring a snack in from home and his mum and dad *always* used to ensure he had a packet of crisps in his bag. To be fair, I remember he used to be quite generous with them, despite the fact that he must have known I'd never be able to return the favour. My dad never got me or my sister any snacks to take into school. I say never, but I do remember this one time when I *did* happen to come to have a bag of crisps with me.

I can't recall whether my dad had got me some or whether I'd just saved up and got some myself, but I remember being really excited knowing I finally had a snack of my own to enjoy at break time. It sounds silly now but when you're a kid, those sorts of things are pretty exciting, especially when you're not used to having many treats. I remember that these particular crisps came in a red packet branded Football Crazy. They were bacon flavoured and ball-shaped. Iain had brought them in before and so I knew I really liked them. Throughout my morning lesson I was *so* looking forward to break time and when the bell sounded, I put my coat on, grabbed the packet of crisps from my bag and joined the mass exodus into the playground. By rights, I should have shared them with Iain, but I knew he'd have his own crisps to enjoy and besides, I was really looking forward to making the most of my special treat.

In those days, all of the boys in the playground used to have the same kind of dark blue or green parka coats, with white fluffy trim around the snorkel hoods, and I was no exception. I remember being stood at the side of the playground with that snorkel hood up and my coat zipped up and the Football Crazy bag of crisps in my eager hands. I was really gonna savour every mouthful of my corn based snack. And I *would* have done, if I'd have had a fucking chance to. In a flash, a miscued pass from the kids playing football nearby resulted in a black and white leather casey hitting me firmly in the stomach. Unfortunately, my packet of crisps had taken the initial impact and I'd heard a fateful 'pop' before the ball hit me. As the football bounced away, I looked down to see the last few remaining bacon flavoured balls fall out of the bottom of the burst bag and collect around my feet. With laughter ringing in my ears, I turned to head towards the rubbish bin. I was filled with an overwhelming sense of crushing disappointment, laced with humiliation. Little did I realise back then, but that incident would be pretty much typical of the way things would go for me for the rest of my life.

One of the last memories I have from that playground in primary school is of this big rounders match we had on the last day of term. I wasn't too excited about playing as I'm a big football fan and not too hot about anything that involves me using my arms. I always hated it when it was approaching summer at school as we'd switch from playing football in P.E., to sports like cricket and rounders. I never understood the point of those games, especially cricket. I mean, in my eyes, unless you're the bowler or the batter, then you're doing nothing other than standing in a field, and that sure isn't fucking sport as far as I'm concerned. You might get the odd opportunity to catch a ball that happens to come your way, but if you drop it then you have to stand there like a daft twat for another hour before you get the chance to make amends.

Everybody had to play in that rounders match on the last day of term and we ended up getting split up into two teams. I spent most of the entire match just stood around, waiting to be told when I'd have to do something. Now, it turns out that I ended up being the last one to bat and, unfortunately for me, there was a bit of pressure on. The scores were level and so it meant that our team would win if I hit the ball well and cleared the bases. Once the rest of the team realised it was me that was up to bat then they quickly tempered their enthusiasm about any possible victory. I was even less confident in me than those fuckers were.

I stood there with the bat in my hands, pretending I had a fucking clue what I was doing, while waiting for the anticipated failure and subsequent groans of disappointment to materialise. It was a girl bowling and I remember being overly conscious that this fact would ensure my humiliation would be even greater. I watched her move to throw and then a second later I swung the bat as hard as I could.

Thwack.

The bat connected perfectly and sent the ball spinning over various heads and into an unmanned area of the field. I stood frozen to the spot for a few seconds in shock, until the rest of my team suddenly started yelling for me to run. I turned on my heels and started to run as fast as my legs could carry me. I couldn't believe it. Nobody could believe it.

I was going to win it for the team. Me!

Unfortunately, I must have been running even faster than my legs could carry me. I'd just got past second base when my legs became tangled and I went sprawling across the hard gravel. The cheers turned to disappointed jeers and everybody began to start trooping off the playground. I was left sat on the floor, staring down at my grazed knee, wondering how it'd all managed to go wrong again.

I learnt a pretty valuable lesson early on during my schooldays. Once a term, the whole class was given the opportunity to escape the drudgery of the classroom and embark on a coach trip to this nature centre for a few days. Coach trips were always tremendously exciting, even when the ultimate destination wasn't. The nature centre wasn't too bad though. It was called 'Parkside Centre' and it was only a few miles away from school. The reason my terrible memory can recollect the name of that place is due to the fact that we had to clap and sing incessantly for the entire fucking duration of the coach journey.

'Parkside Centre is really, really great!'

'Parkside Centre is really, really great!'

It was like some kind of religious mantra and was probably just a psychological weapon utilised by the teaching staff to promote school trips. Because if you were ever asked about that place, no matter how shit a time you'd had, you'd find yourself uttering: –

"Parkside Centre? … It's really, really great."

While we were at that centre, we'd get lessons about wildlife and nature and all that kind of stuff. It wasn't that thrilling and we didn't get to see anything more exotic than frogs and rabbits, but it was miles better than being back at school. During the afternoon of our final day at Parkside Centre, I remember we got asked to draw a picture to illustrate our favourite memory of the trip. I've never been too hot at drawing but I did my best. I can't remember exactly what it was that I drew, but it wouldn't have been very good.

After all the kids had been sketching and colouring in for a while, one of the teachers began walking around the room, passing comment on the work in progress. The teacher was this portly, middle-aged woman with huge spectacles, and I remember she stopped at my work of art and inspected it for a second.

"That's good, Neil, but you just need to spend a bit more time tidying it up and it'll look even better."

It wasn't good *at all*, but I appreciated her tactful critique. Following her comment, she went off to inspect all the other poorly sketched frogs and rabbits around the room and it must have been about fifteen minutes later when the same teacher returned to where I was sat. She picked up my drawing and cast her gaze across it before addressing me with her gap-toothed smile.

"Now, that's a lot better! Well done!"

She put my drawing back down and walked on.

The thing is, I hadn't touched it since her initial appraisal. I wasn't being rebellious or anything, but I'd just got chatting to this kid next to me and, before I knew it, she'd come back.

It was in *exactly* the same fucking state as when she'd first looked at it.

Exactly the same state as when she had decided it needed a bit more work.

So, like I say, I learnt a pretty valuable lesson that day.

People are full of shit.

Chapter Eight

My senior schooldays were spent at this rough comprehensive school in Oldham, near Manchester. I only ended up there because we were living at my dad's shop for about a month and this coincided with the time we had to select schools. As the shop is in Oldham, and therefore our home address was Oldham, I could only choose a school in Oldham. What this meant was that everyone from my primary school went to a school in Manchester and I didn't, which was just bleeding great. School is tough enough, but it helps if you have a few familiar faces there, even if you hate them. I was stuck in this rough comprehensive with a bunch of fucking strangers.

It really is survival of the fittest in the playground. I was desperate just to fade into the background and not bring myself to the attention of any bullies, which is pretty fucking difficult when you're a six foot two inch beanpole with masses of untidy hair. The school itself was quite a dump and was constantly near the bottom of the league tables for school results. The only reason I picked it was that it was ten minutes walk from my dad's shop. It certainly wasn't for the grotesque fucking uniform. Our getup comprised a pair of black trousers and a white shirt, which wasn't bad in itself, but we had to top it all off with an abhorrent tie. It was mainly black, but it had these intermittent slanting red, yellow and green stripes. You can't help but suffer with low self esteem when you're walking about with that eyesore around your neck all day.

There were usually two things that were essential for a teenage boy's credibility in that playground in the nineteen-eighties. One was to be in possession of some expensive branded trainers – preferably Adidas or Nike – and the other was the ability to talk about cars. I knew fuck all about cars and wasn't the slightest bit interested, but what didn't help matters was my dad's choice of vehicle. Boys at school would constantly harp on about cars, and what motor their dad drove, and what the latest registration plate was. Now my dad needed to transport his band equipment about, and all of the speakers and instruments and stuff wouldn't have fit in your normal run of the mill car, so he invested in this ramshackle Land Rover. It was rusty as fuck and was as far removed from the cars the boys in the playground talked about than you could possibly imagine.

At that time, I remember that the latest registration available was one that began with a 'C'. The only reason I still remember that fact is because my dad's glamorous vehicle was also a 'C' reg, only our 'C' was at the end of the number plate as it was an *old* 'C' reg. The automobile industry had moved through the entire fucking alphabet since my dad's car could have last been classed as modern. I used to be fearful of getting spotted in the car on the way to school and would slouch down in my seat to avoid detection. It would probably be a pretty trendy car to be seen in nowadays but back then it was referred to by other teenage boys as 'a pile of shit that only spastics would be seen dead in'. Like I said, kids can be fucking cruel.

There was one stage, towards the beginning of my time in the fourth form, when it seemed like the ridicule regarding my dad's car might be coming to an end. During tea one evening, my dad informed us that he had been talking with my step mum and they had decided they were going to get another car. Apparently, the Land Rover constantly needed to be repaired and was costing him a small fortune.

"So, we're gonna get a normal car then, Dad? Not another Land Rover?"

"No son, not another Land Rover."

I was ecstatic and went to bed that evening fantasising about break times at school and finally being able to join in with the others and talk about our dad's cars, rather than having to sidle off every time the subject was raised. Next morning, for the first time ever, it was me that brought the topic of conversation around to cars.

"Yeah, we're getting a brand new car. It's really cool."

"What kind of car?"

"Well, I'm not sure yet, but my dad's getting it today."

"It'll be shit like that gay Land Rover."

"Shut it, you dick."

"You're the dick, you lanky twat."

We were more than ready for the Oxford Debating Society. This 'friendly' banter was usually the way all of our playground conversations went. Still, this time I'd be the one having the last laugh.

I couldn't wait to finish school that day and see our new car and wave goodbye to that decrepit Land Rover. I remember running out of the school gates and arriving at my dad's shop out of breath but full of excitement. I told you I'm not really bothered about cars but I was sick of having to keep my head down any time that we went out in that Land Rover.

"Have we got the car then, Dad?"

"Yeah, it's outside at the back. Go and have a look."

I rushed through the shop; past the old women in the Ladies' side and out through the large, wooden gate at the back. I remember the Land Rover was still there, but parked behind it was our new car: a shiny Robin Reliant. I don't know if you know anything about cars, but a Robin Reliant has one unique feature that differentiates it from all other cars. It only has three wheels. *Three* fucking wheels. A Robin Reliant was the joke of the car world – even I knew that. If cars had ever had to go to school, the Robin Reliant would have been the one that got bullied. My dad had managed to pick us a more embarrassing car than the hundred year old Land Rover. I wanted to puke.

There were numerous occasions when my childhood was made even more of a psychological trauma than it needed to be. I wanted to tell you about this other time when we'd just arrived home at night after being at school all day. We always went through the same routine, where we'd have to go upstairs and change out of our uniforms and then come back downstairs to face whatever appetising dish my step mum had just reheated for us. This particular night, we sat down at the table and my step mum informed me that she'd been out shopping that day and had managed to get me some trainers. I knew very fucking well that there was absolutely no chance of being presented with a pair of sparkling new black Adidas Sambas, and that I'd have the cheapest trainers in existence.

To tell you the truth, I wasn't at all fucking bothered about having expensive trainers. I would have just been happy with some mid-price, generic ones that would end up in me receiving mild snorts of derision in the changing room. She had managed to outdo herself though. Now, I need you to realise that back in the mid to late eighties, all trainers were either black or dark blue with white stripes or swoosh logos. They definitely weren't anything like the sight that greeted me when I lifted the lid off that box of new trainers. They were completely yellow with yellow stripes. *Bright fucking yellow. Bullied to fuck yellow.*

There was a sticker on the sole of each trainer that read 'Dunlop Superstars' although I doubt whether Dunlop had anything to do with the manufacture of those monstrosities and I doubt even more whether they'd ever gotten near the feet of any superstars. I felt sick to the pit of my stomach. I even had to thank her for them.

"They were really cheap as well."

I bet they fucking were.

Two days later I was in the changing room for P.E., deliberately taking my time in a vain attempt to delay the unveiling of my *beautiful* trainers. There was no chance I'd be the last one out though 'cos there was always two or three boys that had reached puberty before everybody else and those fuckers liked to stroll about the changing room naked, thrusting their hips forward to proudly show off their developed penises and freshly sprouted pubic hair. They sure as fuck made the rest of us feel inadequate, but that was their intention. I hastily tucked my underdeveloped acorn away in my shorts and then began to slowly pull up each football sock, whilst staring at the cheap sports bag which held those luminous yellow trainers.

I kept wondering about how I could accidentally lose them on purpose. She'd fucking know I'd done it intentionally though. I knew that there was no avoiding it and, as I sat with the last few stragglers in the changing room, I reached inside the bag and pulled each trainer out one by one. Unbelievably, they seemed to look even more hideous and garish than before.

"Ha. What the fuck are they? Hey, look at his trainers."

Cunts. It was even worse when I sidled out onto the football pitch into the daylight and the full glare of twenty-eight teenage wannabe comedians. I could even sense the derision in the look my P.E. teacher gave those trainers and I spent the next fifty-two minutes doing my absolute utmost to destroy them. I dragged and scraped them through the mud and raked them against the goalpost when it was my turn to go in goal. By the end of the P.E. lesson, those trainers were caked in mud and didn't seem quite so gaudy as when I'd first pulled them out of the bag. I was quite satisfied that in a week or two they would be torn and shoddy enough, with all but the tiniest bit of yellow left on show.

When I got home that evening, I threw my P.E. kit in the dirty washing basket and gave my trainers a few stabs with my maths compass before launching them under my bed. I trundled downstairs and sat at the table unable to contain myself at the thought of the sumptuous feast that was about to be served up by my step mum. As I sat there, pushing dried cabbage about my plate, she started to speak.

"Where's your P.E. kit?"

"In the washing basket."

"What about your new trainers?"

"Under my bed."

"I meant to tell you. Seeing that they were so cheap, I got you two pairs."

For Fuck's sake. I don't know if she actually understood the torment she was causing me but it wouldn't have fucking surprised me if she did.

I was quite good at football, despite my footwear, and I even managed to make the school team. The P.E. teacher would usually pick the team and he'd put the line-up on a sheet of paper and pin it on a notice board in the main school hall. I'm not that confident an individual really and I never expected to get picked. I *didn't* get picked for the first four or five matches they had.

I remember one Thursday morning though, when this kid walked past me in the corridor and asked whether I knew I'd been picked for the team. I assumed he was taking the piss and told him so, and he directed me towards the notice board to see for myself. My heart was racing as I made my way across. I didn't believe him but I thought it was a bit of a weird thing to wind someone up about all the same. I got to the board and, sure enough, the team sheet had been pinned up for the match on the forthcoming Saturday. I scanned the names from one to eleven until I reached the list of substitutes at the bottom. I took a large gulp of air. *There it was! My name!* We'd had a P.E. lesson the previous day and I knew I'd played quite well but I hadn't considered for one minute that I'd make the team sheet. It was the kind of thing that didn't happen to me.

I couldn't wait to tell my mum and dad about getting picked. They both seemed really pleased. It's a good feeling when you think you've done something to make your parents proud. I was due to be at my mum's that weekend and she said she was gonna come and watch me, along with my sister. My uncle, being a big football fan, was made up with the news and said he was gonna accompany us too. On the Friday evening, I went to bed fantasising about coming on to the pitch and waltzing through the opposition defence before scoring the winning goal and turning to see the joyous reactions of my trio of fans.

The match was being played on the school fields, which meant the four of us had to get a bus into town, and then another bus to the school, near my dad's shop. My dad's shop was open on Saturdays and I would have liked him to have come too, but I knew he couldn't 'cos of work. Prior to the game, we called in at the shop for a cup of tea. My uncle started chatting to my dad about how exciting it was and I remember feeling incredibly nervous and anxious that I was gonna disappoint them somehow. I tried to play it down and told them I was only substitute and might not even get to play, but it didn't seem to dampen my uncle's enthusiasm. It was when we were all sat around in the kitchen, in the back of the shop, waiting for the kettle to boil, that I first started to have a nagging worry in the back of my mind.

I'd told everyone that the match kicked off at eleven and it was a quarter to ten when we were sat in that kitchen, so by my reckoning we had plenty of time. The thing is, I started to suddenly question whether the kick off was actually ten, not eleven. I kept trying to picture the team sheet in my mind. The kick off time had been at the bottom. The more I thought about it, the more I started to convince myself that I'd got it wrong and the kick off *was* at ten. I didn't want to voice my concern to anyone, as if saying it out loud would give the theory some credibility. I hurried everyone up though and told them to rush their drinks 'cos I wanted to get there early.

It was about five past ten when we approached the school gates and the path leading off to the football pitches. The closer we had gotten to school, the more I became convinced that I'd messed up. As we arrived within viewing distance of the pitches, I could see that a game was already taking place. I quickened my pace and began to feel nauseous as my concerns became a reality. The match was underway. I'd got it all wrong. My mum, my uncle and my sister had come all this way to see me and I'd fucked it all up. I remember I broke into a run and sprinted towards the pitch and to where the P.E. teacher was stood. He gave me a cursory glance before returning to focus on the match.

"You're late."

"I'm sorry, Sir. I… I thought it was eleven o'clock kick off."

"No. Ten."

He wasn't best pleased. I remember turning to see my mum, uncle and sister nearing the pitch. I turned back to the teacher.

"Shall I still get changed?"

He answered, but kept his eyes on the football match.

"No. It's too late."

It *wasn't* too fucking late but he obviously wanted to punish me for not arriving on time. He still wasn't looking at me and I turned away slowly to walk towards where my expectant relatives were stood.

"What's happened?"

"I got the time wrong. It kicked off at ten. Not eleven."

Tears were welling up inside me. I felt a fucking idiot and I knew I'd let them all down. They'd come all that way for nothing. My uncle and sister were silent. My mum came up with her usual reassuring response when things went wrong.

"Never mind."

Much to my amazement, I got picked as substitute for the next match. I managed to make it on time, although my mum, my uncle and my sister didn't ever come to watch me again.

Chapter Nine

My best friend at school was this guy called Robert and he was the captain of the football team. He would always wear the latest cool trainers and carry a trendy Slazenger sports bag. He was one of those kids that was great academically *and* amazing on the sports field too. He really was the golden boy. All the teachers loved him and he always seemed totally confident chatting with the girls. He had ginger hair, so wasn't the stereotypical high school hunk that you see in those American films, but he seemed to get away with it somehow. Obviously things were different in Chadderton than in California.

Looking back, he was a bit of a bastard to me and I can't understand for the life of me how we were friends. We had absolutely nothing in common and I can't recollect even one tiny, good memory about him. I must have just been sat next to him when we first started school, or maybe he just liked being next to me 'cos it made him think he looked better standing next to a lanky clown in cheap clothes and even cheaper shoes.

The two abiding memories I have of Robert both involve him being an absolute twat. There was this one time, during a history lesson, when he had been sat at the desk behind me in the classroom. Our history teacher back then was a complete pervert. He must have been in his fifties but he used to leer and try and flirt with the girls in our class. It was pretty sickening the way he'd slime all over the prettier girls, and he'd be a right bastard to the boys and the ugly girls. This one lesson, he'd been droning on at the front of the class, when I felt this sharp pain in my back. I turned around and Robert was sniggering. My *fantastic* best friend had lined up his plastic ruler on the edge of his desk and had used it to prod me in the back. I glared at him and turned back around and immediately felt another sharp dig in my back. I turned around again and grabbed his ruler and threw it at him.

"YOU BOY! WHAT ARE YOU DOING?"

The history teacher was standing and staring at me.

"Nothing, Sir."

"COME HERE AT ONCE!"

My heart was racing and I looked at Robert in the hope he'd speak up and explain how it hadn't *actually* been my fault. He didn't say a word. I remember getting gingerly to my feet and feeling my legs shaking as I walked all the way to the front of the class.

"Nobody messes about in my class. Put your hand out."

I looked up at him for some sign of compassion but the whites of his eyes were bulging in rage and I knew there was no getting out of it. I'd never been in trouble before. I was a really quiet, unassuming kid and I'd always kept my nose clean. Now I was about to get the strap. I slowly reached out with my hand and he gripped this leather belt and swung it with some force across the palm of my hand. Almost immediately, a second lashing followed.

"NOW GET BACK TO YOUR SEAT!"

I started the long walk back to my desk and I could sense my cheeks were bright red and tears were welling up in my eyes. It wasn't so much because of the pain of the punishment I had received, but more because of the humiliation. I knew everyone was staring at me and I remember deliberately not looking any of them in the eye. If I had done, then I knew I'd have burst into tears and that would have been even more humiliating than getting strapped.

Sometimes I ended up getting humiliated through nobody's fault but my own. I remember one Geography lesson when the teacher had asked us to start shouting out as many countries as possible that made up the continent of South America. Geography wasn't a strong subject for me and my knowledge of life outside of the United Kingdom was pretty much non-existent. A lot of the other kids at school had been on holidays abroad but I'd never been on an aeroplane. Hey, come to think of it, I *did* go abroad once. Unbelievably, my dad stumped up the cash to send me on a day trip to Boulogne with school. I remember the kids running riot on the ferry before we got there, and the day not being overly productive even when we arrived on French soil. We spent half the time taking turns to queue up at a bakery and request pain and fromage in pidgin French from an exasperated shopkeeper. The rest of the day was spent waiting for the girls to queue for the toilets. The boy's toilet was free – understandably as it was pretty much just a wall. The girl's toilet was one franc and the school budget obviously couldn't cover the expense so each girl had to do their business and then hold the door open for the next in line. It wasn't the most culturally stimulating of afternoons. My abiding memory is of failing to pass off my five centime coin as five francs in order to acquire a tacky Eiffel Tower shaped container of cheap perfume from a street trader for my mum. That French peddler had some morals though. He could have made a small fortune if he hadn't refused to sell the boys of South Chadderton Comprehensive School his entire stock of pornographic playing cards

Usually the only times I'd have the opportunity to venture outside of the North West of England were trips to the arse-end of Scotland or Wales. For a long time, holidays brought back nightmare memories of being cooped up in the back of the Land Rover for hours with my awful extended family, eating boiled egg sandwiches and listening to my dad and step mum arguing. We'd finally arrive in the middle of nowhere, where it'd be typically freezing cold with nothing to do. We'd spend a miserable week as the arguments continued before commencing the long journey home. Anyway, my lack of foreign holidays doesn't really excuse my fuck-up in Geography that day. My love of football and Panini sticker albums ensured I had some geographical knowledge and some ill-founded confidence.

"Mexico" I cried out that day.

"Peru".

I was becoming increasingly cocksure.

"Uruguay".

"Paraguay".

I should have quit while I was ahead. I knew one of the first lessons of surviving school unscathed was to keep your head below the parapet. I'd become lost in my haste to show off my World Cup related trivia.

"Portugal".

I remember the laughter immediately broke out, growing to a crescendo as my face reddened. I had nowhere to run. Just like the rounders game, I'd crashed and burned and managed to snatch defeat from the jaws of victory. To the credit of my Geography teacher, he made a vain effort to save my blushes by explaining how it was an understandable mistake because of the links between Portugal and South America. He must have spent the next 30 minutes deviating from his lesson plan to explain them. I learned to keep my hand down in future lessons and to realise that some teachers are pretty decent human beings.

Although I'll readily admit to having loads of faults, one positive attribute I *do* have is good manners. My mum and dad brought me up to be polite and, even today, I'll still hold doors open for people and always say 'please' and 'thank you'. In my opinion though, I'm *too* fucking nice and polite at times. For instance, I'll apologise for things that happen in life, even if it's not my fault. I'm *always* apologising. If someone bumps into me in the street, then I'll automatically say 'sorry', even if it's no fault of my own. You know sometimes when you're walking into a building and somebody is coming out and you both go in the same direction and end up doing some kind of crazy dance? I'll immediately apologise even though I'm, *at the most*, fifty per cent responsible for the confusion.

I remember one break time at school when we'd all been lining up outside the classroom waiting to go in. I was stood next to Robert, just minding my own business, when he suddenly decided to pick a fight with me. I don't know what the fuck his problem was, but he turned and started pushing me hard in the chest. He'd been beaten up a few weeks earlier in the playground and the only thing I can think of is that he wanted to get a bit of self-respect back. He obviously fancied his chances of being able to beat me up and get some reverence back from the playground. Now, I've since listened to Dionne Warwick belting out 'That's What Friends Are For' loads of times, and not once does she mention twatting them in the playground.

As you can imagine, I was more than a bit shocked when my best friend started pushing me and hitting me for absolutely no reason whatsoever. I didn't even defend myself for a second because I was so taken aback. He was pushing me and hitting me and shouting abuse and it didn't take long before the other kids noticed. Back then, all the children would gather around in a circle if there were two kids fighting. The little fuckers would revel in it and they'd all start chanting to bring it to the attention of all the other kids who'd yet to spot the outbreak of violence. When I was at school in Manchester, the kids would gather around scraps shouting:

"FIGHT, FIGHT, FIGHT!"

In Oldham, because of some strange, unfathomable variation in local dialect, they'd instead shout:

"BARNEY, BARNEY, BARNEY!"

I hated watching any kids fighting, let alone being the poor bastard getting pummelled in front of a baying crowd. I didn't wanna fight and I didn't wanna be in front of that horde of kids. In order to protect myself more than anything, I remember I lurched across and managed to get him in a headlock. By rights, I should have floored the bastard and kicked ten bells out of him, but I didn't. I just held him in that headlock so that he couldn't get at me. Seconds later, his Maths teacher came storming across the playground, barking at us to separate. As was the norm, all the other kids quickly dispersed, leaving us two to stand there and face the music.

"What do you think you're doing?"

We both just looked at the floor.

"Who started it?"

I looked at him, but I remember he just kept his head bowed, staring straight at the ground.

"Come on. I want to know who started the fight."

I looked sideways again at him. I knew that bastard wasn't going to say a word. I just wanted to get out of the situation and go back to class and so I spoke up.

"I started it, Miss."

I'd done fuck all, apart from act as a punching bag, but I just felt like accepting responsibility would get it all over with and allow us to get back to the classroom and away from the mocking faces of schoolkids walking by. And I guess I thought he'd apologise afterwards and start acting better towards me. He fucking didn't though and I just ended up with a detention. I wish I *had* kicked ten bells out of that bastard.

I told you I was pretty quiet at school. I tried to keep my head down and I just hung around with a small, core group of pals. There was my 'best friend' Robert that I just told you about; this kid Tony who was best pals with a boy called Michael; and this other kid named John, who was part of our group but hadn't been allocated a best friend. He was a nice enough kid and he had this mop of curly hair, brown eyes and this wide, boxer's nose. He hadn't crossed my mind for ages, to be honest, until a few years ago when that serial killer Fred West was all over the news. When I saw the first pictures of Fred West, I immediately thought how much he resembled John.

He lived fairly close to school in an end terraced house, and we used to go there quite a lot at lunchtimes. He was pretty scruffy and you could tell from his house that he wasn't particularly well off, although I guess none of us were, except maybe Robert. He did have this pool table though in his front room, so we used to play a bit at lunchtimes. Unfortunately the room wasn't quite big enough to use the cue properly for some shots. The other pitfall was this mongrel dog he had that was obviously never toilet trained and had usually crapped in at least one part of the room. In all the times I'd watch Steve Davis or Cliff Thorburn on TV they'd occasionally have an awkward angle to hit a ball and have to use one of those spider rests. Not once did

I see them at the Crucible having to cue at a 90 degree angle against a wall or manoeuvre around dog turds.

Other times we'd watch videos in his front room – mainly horror films. This overweight Asian kid in our class used to get us these dodgy films from his dad's video shop. We watched loads of videos over the years but the only one that clearly sticks in my mind is this werewolf movie called *The Howling*. The reason I remember it isn't down to any scintillating plot or award-winning cinematography; it's purely because there's this one scene where a gorgeous, dark-haired woman does a nude full-frontal in the middle of a forest. We were all made up with that scene. I don't think we ever got to see the end of the film 'cos we spent the remainder of the lunch hour just rewinding back to that flash of pubic hair. Its golden memories like those that I'll cherish in my old age.

As John let us go back to his house to play pool and watch films, you'd be forgiven for thinking he'd be quite the toast of our gang and the recipient of much admiration. Nothing could be further from the truth though, 'cos we used to spend the majority of our free time verbally abusing each other. I suppose all kids do the same kind of thing. He was pilloried for being scruffy and if there was anything on TV that gave us ammunition, then we wouldn't hesitate to let rip. I think he was mightily relieved the day the television adaptation of *Stig of the Dump* finished. He wasn't the brightest kid on the block though and didn't help himself by telling somebody that he'd wanked his dog off one day. I don't know why he did that to his dog, and I know even less why he felt the need to tell someone, but it was soon all over the school. Apart from the dog fondling incident, he was a pretty good guy.

Tony was quite a clever kid but he was always down in the dumps about something or other. He had loads of freckles and golden hair, but it was pretty thin so he would constantly get abuse about being bald. And that was from his mates. I swear, we were all a real bunch of cunts. I remember he came into school one day and he was even more miserable than usual. It turned out his pet rabbit had died in the night and he was pretty cut up about it. If he thought for a moment though that his trusty band of pals would offer a sympathetic ear, then he was sadly mistaken. Somebody initiated a chorus of the theme to *Watership Down* and it wasn't long before almost every pupil at that school would burst into a rendition of 'Bright Eyes' whenever he walked past. I swear the kids at that school were fucking psychological terrorists.

It wouldn't have surprised me if he'd have gone on to commit suicide after leaving that place, but he obviously hadn't 'cos unfortunately I ran into him again at a wedding, a year or so ago. I swear after ten minutes of listening to him whine on about his life, I was the one who felt like killing himself. I remember he was saying how his wife had recently left him. I acted all shocked about it, but the only thing I was shocked about was the fact he'd gotten someone to marry him in the first place. It's awful being out and about and bumping into somebody you know 'cos you can't ignore them the way you can with strangers. It's bad enough seeing someone you know in the street but at least you can usually just let on and then walk away as fast as fucking possible. When you're stuck at some place, like a wedding, then there's no escape.

While he was wallowing in self pity, I remembered one evening during our schooldays, when he'd phoned me at home. It was strange 'cos, thankfully, he usually only ever spoke to me at school. My step mum had turned the TV down, as per fucking usual, and passed me the phone. He sounded a bit nervy and it took him a while to get around to the reason for the call. It turned out that he was thinking of asking my sister out on a date and wanted to make sure I was okay with it. It was a pretty noble fucking gesture but it was totally unnecessary. I really couldn't have given a fuck whether he'd asked her out or not. Besides, if every guy who my sister went out with rang to ask permission first, then I'd never be off the fucking phone. She wasn't too choosy, my sister, but to be fair to her she still had the tactical nous to give that miserable fucker a wide berth.

The last guy in the group was Mike, who was the best of the bunch and, surprisingly enough, ended up a pretty good friend of mine. I say surprising, 'cos we weren't that close at school and, as I said, for some strange reason he was best friends with Miserable Tony. Michael was probably the only one of the group that didn't get much grief when it came to name-calling sessions. There wasn't anything obvious that stood out about him that we could latch onto, so although he joined in the vicious verbal assaults on others, he pretty much got away with it himself. Like I told you before, John had his scruffy angle, Robert got the ginger stuff and Tony got all the bald lines. I was a tall, gangly fucker so anything to do with being skinny came my way. I remember to this day the first time I saw an advert for Scotch videotape where they had this skeleton singing that Rolling Stones song 'Not Fade Away'. I knew my 'friends' would be on it like a shot and sure enough, the following Monday, it was belted out as soon as I walked into the classroom.

It didn't help when even the teachers gave them ammunition. I remember one time when we had all started this new German class. The teacher was a painfully thin, German woman who looked like a pretty good transvestite. She had this really piercing, heavily accented voice. Anyway, at the start of term, she decided that it would be great fun if we all adopted German forenames instead of our usual English names. Other boys got tame stuff like Karl or Stefan. I got Norbert. As you can imagine, it didn't take the rest of the class seconds before it was tweaked to 'Nobhead'. Their rapier-like wit knew no bounds. Me and Helmut took a lot of fucking stick in those classes.

Chapter Ten

I was absolutely fucking terrified of girls when I was at school. I knew that I liked them physically, and I knew from those magazines that they definitely held all the cards in the cruel game of Life. Looking myself up and down in the mirror after a shower, I couldn't contemplate in a million years that I'd be able to convince a girl to show me 'theirs' in exchange for a glimpse of the sight before me. It's no surprise then that my success rate with girls in those days was pretty fucking poor.

The first time I can recall ever having any kind of feelings for a girl was way back in primary school. The relationship was probably doomed from the start due to the fact that the girl I desired was actually a woman in her early-twenties and I must have been about seven or eight. She was a teacher by the name of Miss Hill and I'm pretty sure that the age gap *might* have been an issue for her. It's difficult to describe what my feelings towards her must have been 'cos I damn sure wasn't sexually aware at that age and my idea of a hot date would likely have involved us eating sherbet dip dabs and watching *Top Cat*. I liked being around her and remember feeling differently about her than anybody I had ever met in my life, up to that point. It sounds ridiculous admitting this now, but I can remember vividly during assembly one morning when my young self was dealt what would become a familiar emotional battering. Following on from our hymns and the usual blathering from the Headteacher, we were informed of the 'wonderful' news that Miss Hill had recently married and was now to be addressed by everybody as Mrs Carter. The bitch had been carrying on with somebody behind my back.

I told you I loved playing football at school but there was a short period of time in the early nineteen-eighties when I became an avid follower of televised rugby. We never played rugby when I was younger and initially I never warmed to it if I caught it on TV – largely 'cos I couldn't follow the rules and therefore didn't have a fucking clue what was going on. I must have been about ten or so when I learned to appreciate the advantages of watching that particular sport. It was one Saturday afternoon when they were showing an England game at Twickenham on *Grandstand*. I couldn't tell you who they were playing, what the score was, or what *any* of the players' names were. In fact I only remember *one* name from that day – Erika Roe. I was probably barely watching the match that day but thankfully glanced up at just the right moment. Even my flimsy grasp of the rules and regulations of rugby union was enough to understand there was something amiss when a topless woman with huge tits strode onto the field of play. These days, broadcasters tend to ensure that any disruptions to live televised events are kept out of camera shot. Not in the nineteen-eighties though. I got an eyeful of Erika and my sexual awakening had begun. She got a fair bit of fame 'cos of that streak and I don't think I missed another televised rugby match for the next four years.

I had intense, passionate relationships with two girls in secondary school, although neither of them knew a bleeding thing about it. I chose to worship from afar and kid myself that I'd be with them one day. I was safe in the knowledge that for that to happen I'd have to speak to them, and I knew that was never gonna happen in a million years. Emotionally, they were quite safe relationships to be in. I could be completely in love and have that nice feeling of butterflies in my stomach and all that crap. As they didn't actually *know* I existed, there was no way they could ruin things by, for example, refusing to actually *be* my girlfriend. In a completely fucked up way, I envy how it was back then and that whole simplistic attitude I had towards what a relationship should be.

The first girl I can remember having a crush on was this girl called Hannah. She was in almost all of my classes throughout secondary school. The only class I *didn't* share with her was maths, 'cos that was the only subject I struggled with and it meant I'd had to drop down a set. She was pretty unremarkable looking to be honest, but there was something about her I really liked. She had a nice smile and lovely long, dark brown hair. I never actually talked to her once during my whole time at that school, although I looked at her an awful lot. She seemed a pleasant enough kind of girl and was one of the more intelligent kids at that place. I remember it always bothered me when my best friend Robert used to ask her about homework, 'cos it was obviously just an excuse to talk to her. I half suspected that my *brilliant* pal had cottoned on to the fact I had feelings for her and therefore thought he'd get in there first.

I remember I used to scrawl her initials 'heart' my initials under the desk during lessons. I knew nobody would ever see it but it sort of gave the relationship a bit more weight in my eyes, if you know what I mean. It also says a lot about my rebellious, bad boy persona at school that my one attempt at graffiti was cowardly doodled in a place that I knew would never get me into trouble. Anyway, Hannah didn't appear to notice me in the *entire* time I was at school. On the odd occasion that she did catch me looking, I'd swiftly look away and glance everywhere but in her direction. I was that shy and worried she'd seen me that I'd avoid looking at her for a few days in the hope that it would put her off the scent.

I knew that she lived relatively close to the school, and that her father owned a newsagents. One weekend, when I was staying at my mum's in the opposite end of Manchester, I hatched this harebrained scheme to go all the way to that shop and to march in and ask her to go out with me. I rehearsed it in my mind about a billion times. I'd fantasise about how I'd walk in and act all cool and then, when she was hanging on my every word, I'd just blurt out that I wanted to take her on a date. I remember I got this pal of mine, Kevin, to come all the way across Manchester with me to see her. He lived near my mum and we'd gotten friendly after he'd walked past me one day while I was kicking a football against a neighbour's wall. Being the introverted bastard I am, I sure as fuck wouldn't have talked to him but he was with my sister and this friend that she had made, so they made the introductions and that was that. Anyway, he'd agreed to come with me that day, which was pretty good of him 'cos it was a long fucking journey and we had to get two separate bus rides there and back.

By the time we'd gotten on the second bus to our destination, I remember I was already starting to feel nervous as hell and pretty much knew things weren't gonna go to plan. We got off the bus in Oldham and started walking towards where I knew her dad's shop was located. To be quite frank, having Kevin there with me wasn't the big bleeding help I thought it would be. I felt even more pressured and I realised the chances were that I'd not only end up feeling a right idiot, but that I'd have someone else there to witness the whole shameful experience.

We turned a corner and I spotted the shop on the end of a row of terraced houses. The door was open, which enabled me to walk past a ridiculous amount of times and see whether she was about. She *was* there, and she was there on her own. I'd been desperately praying for an excuse to be able to abort the mission, but it was to no avail. I remember I made several attempts to walk into the shop, before turning swiftly around each time and returning to my friend. If she'd have spotted me she'd either have thought I was about to commit an armed robbery, or that I was absolutely mental. Neither of them was the romantic vision of me I'd wanted her to have.

After an amount of time I'm too embarrassed to admit to, I finally took a big gulp of air and strode through the shop door. I can recall it was quite pokey inside and there was nobody else about but me and her. To be honest, I couldn't even glance up to where I knew she was stood. I had become a complete nervous wreck. I scanned the confectionary in front of me before hastily picking up a Mars bar that I didn't even want. I still couldn't look up, let alone speak, as I handed her my pound coin. I snatched the chocolate bar and my change and turned sharply out of that shop and I didn't stop until we were back at the bus stop. It hadn't gone to plan, but the fact I'd not asked her out meant that she wasn't able to say no and I could continue being in love with her. I never did get to speak to her although I remained true to her for about another four terms. Right up until one September morning when she turned up to class after a summer break with a long, shaggy perm. I ended the relationship there and then.

The only *other* girl that I held a torch for at school was the total opposite of Hannah. She wasn't in any of my classes, apart from the maths one that I had to drop down into. She definitely wasn't the brightest spark, and again she wasn't particularly all that pretty, but there was something about her that appealed to me. Whereas Hannah was relatively quiet and demure, Janine was quite loud and brash. Even at the tender age of fourteen, she had a reputation of being a bit of a slapper. To be frank, I'm pretty sure that's what my attraction to her was borne out of. I desperately wanted to get some and she seemed a much safer bet than Hannah, although the reality was that I had fuck all chance with her either.

I went through all the same behaviour as with Hannah; the fantasising, the scrawling under the desk, the yearning gazes, et cetera. I even tried to enlist the services of my sister in an attempt to get close to her, by asking her to make friends with Janine. There was even one stage when I thought things *might* have been going to plan. My sister had managed to get a bit friendly with her and subsequently told me she'd invited her to stay over at our mum's house, one weekend. Six days of incessant fantasies later, only for my sister to inform me that it wouldn't be happening after all. Apparently they'd fallen out after Janine had 'borrowed' some jewellery from my sister and failed to return it. Now you might think that having my love interest depicted as some kind of thieving slag by all and sundry would have dampened my ardour somewhat, but nothing could have been further from the truth.

Developments with our relationship came to a head late one afternoon, as a maths lesson was coming to an end. Whereas Hannah seemed to be totally oblivious to my affection for her, it seemed as if Janine was all too aware of my feelings. That afternoon, she came over to me and asked could she borrow my maths book as she had missed the last lesson and wanted to catch up. I was more than willing to take the risk of my maths book going the same way as my sister's jewellery and gleefully handed it over. I spent the whole weekend on a high. *Why did she ask to borrow my maths book? – I'm shit at maths – she must like me!*

Following the longest weekend of my short life, I headed for my maths lesson on the Monday filled with nervous trepidation. She'd have to give me my maths book back and so I knew I was going to have contact with her. *Maybe we'd drum up a conversation and I'd come up with some great witticisms and she'd throw her head back and laugh with great gusto before leaning forward and whispering in my ear that she couldn't resist me and would have to have me at the earliest opportunity?* It turned out she didn't show up though. She wasn't the most studious of classmates and used to skip school fairly often. I'd have to wait until the next maths class on the following Wednesday.

When the day of destiny arrived, I walked into class and made my way to my desk, furtively glancing about to see if she'd turned up. It wasn't long before I heard her booming voice addressing one of her friends, as she made her way into the room. A couple of minutes later, I looked around as my maths book came whizzing towards me though the air after she'd tossed it disconcertingly in my direction. She carried on chatting to her friends while I turned back to inspect the newly-returned workbook. It looked a bit more tattered and dog-eared than when I'd last seen it. I remember slowly thumbing through the pages, anxiously searching for some hidden declaration of her love for me. There was nothing whatsoever until I flipped the book so that the back cover was in view.

There, scrawled in biro across the back, was a crude drawing of a heart with an arrow through. It contained the following proclamation in large lettering:

'*Janine loves Craig*'.

Now the one thing you've learnt so far in this story is that my name is *not* fucking Craig. I felt crushed at this revelation and her act of betrayal. Being a big fucking wimp though, that emotion was soon replaced by the nagging worry that I might get into trouble for the rudimentary sketch now adorning the back of my exercise book.

Chapter Eleven

Towards the last year or so of school, when I was about fifteen, I started to go out to bars and nightclubs at weekends. The friend that I told you about, Kevin, was a couple of years older than me and it was him that began taking me out. He'd recently started going out clubbing and was having a bit of success with women and so I was more than happy to tag along. I remember the first time we went out into Manchester on a Saturday night. He'd arranged for us to meet up with these two girls that he knew. That afternoon, my mental composition was one part excitement, two parts shitting myself.

I didn't really have anything to wear and I couldn't afford to go out and buy any trendy clothes. I ended up wearing these black pants that were way too short, along with this incredibly cheap, awful green and white striped shirt that I'd bought from the local market earlier that day. I doused my hair with half a can of my mum's Silvikrin hairspray for some reason to top my *fantastically* stylish look off. I must have looked an absolute cunt. I remember being nervous as hell and Kev made things even worse by telling me that we might get grilled on the door by the bouncers. He told me that if they didn't think we were eighteen, then they might ask us a bunch of questions and that I should just stay calm and lie my way in. I already told you I can't lie.

That evening, we got the bus into town and made our way over to Champers Wine Bar where we were supposed to be meeting the girls. We walked straight into the bar without the bouncers even raising an eyebrow. There's no way that I could have passed for eighteen but, judging by the clientele inside that place, I'm not sure they were too fussy about *who* they let in. The bar was in the basement of this office building and we had to walk down a steep stairway before my low-rent shoes finally made contact with the equally low-rent carpeted floor area of the bar. The place was quite dark and only illuminated by occasional pink and blue neon lighting. I was *unbelievably* nervous and let him lead the way to the bar. The bar staff must have been in awe of the two hardened fucking drinkers stood in front of them as Kev confidently ordered us two halves of cider.

While we were waiting for our drinks I looked anxiously around and saw two girls waving across in our direction. Kev waved back and passed me my drink, and I followed him across to where the girls were seated. They had their backs to this really tacky mirrored wall and we sat in our seats across from them, with this sparkly, metal rimmed table between us. They both looked happy to see him and I could tell they were giving me the once over. He'd already told me the girls were called Sophie and Natalie and he introduced us properly once we'd sat down. He'd also already made it clear that Sophie was his date and Natalie was therefore mine, by default. To be truthful, at that age, I'd have been happy with *any* woman in town.

Sophie was quite pretty and had this wavy blonde

hair and a nice genuine smile. Natalie on the other hand looked a bit of a bitch. She wasn't great looking really but, to be fair, she had an amazing body. She was miserable looking and had long jet black hair, but what sticks in my mind the most was that she was wearing this really short dress. And because she was sat down in that really short dress, you could quite clearly see her little white knickers. That obviously sticks in my mind because I'm a Grade A pervert, but to a fifteen year old boy that vision was a fucking sight for sore eyes. I'd have been quite happy to just sit there all weekend looking at those white knickers. I continued to sit there for the next half an hour, not really saying anything whilst Kevin chatted confidently with the girls. I was conscious that I couldn't really stare at her knickers but I was content just knowing that they were there if I wanted to look.

After we'd all finished our drinks, we left that bar and started to walk towards Branagans, this other awful bar across town. I was still nervous and uneasy and felt really uncomfortable about the whole situation – and I still didn't have a fucking clue what to say to those girls. My awkwardness wasn't helped by Natalie, who had already made it pretty fucking clear that she was about as into me as much as she'd be into a case of thrush.

When we got to Branagans, the bastard bouncer started giving me hassle about being underage and the girls and Kevin had to talk him into allowing me in. I could've done without that additional fucking embarrassment, thanks very much. When we eventually walked in, Sophie went to the toilet and Kevin went to the bar, so I was left stood alone with Natalie. She wasn't talking to me *at all*, but I felt pressured into saying something to her. I just didn't know *what* though. My first instinct was to ask her 'Do you come here often?', but *even* I knew that was a renowned cheesy line and so I came up with an ingenious alternative.

"Do you come here a lot?"

I could tell she wasn't impressed. She gave me a pretty fucking frosty look.

"No."

That was about as chatty as we got. I just sat there silent, pretty much the whole night, hoping for another glance at those white knickers. It turns out that Kevin had previously had a bit of fun with that Natalie girl but had moved onto her friend, Sophie. Natalie was still hot for Kevin and so my chances with her had been pretty fucking limited, even if I'd not dressed and acted like a gormless twat. I later found out through Kevin that she'd called me 'hanging' in a subsequent telephone conversation. That did wonders for my fucking confidence, I can tell you. She was a bit of a bitch with me that night, and I'd been no nearer to getting any action, but I'll still always hold her in fond regard for happily flashing those white knickers.

Going to bars and clubs at the weekend got to be quite a regular occurrence in those days. The main driver was always the desire to meet a girl, although it still seemed at the time like it was just a fucking pipedream. The thing was, I was bleeding hopeless at chatting women up. I still am now. I could never understand what the fuck you were supposed to say when you went up to a total stranger. Whatever

I thought of sounded really lame to me, and I always put myself in the girl's shoes and imagined if someone came up to *me* spouting crap then I'd just want them to fuck off as far away as possible.

I really analyse things way too much. It's a big confidence thing with me too. I know some guys who could ask out every single girl in a club, and get rejections every time, and yet *still* not think twice about bowling up to the next girl they saw. It takes me *forever* to go up to someone and if I get a rejection then I spend the next fortnight worrying and obsessing over why they didn't like me. I swear, I'm fucking crazy.

Some girls put you at ease straight away when you go up to them, but some are right bastards. It's like being in front of Simon *fucking* Cowell with some girls. They just glare at you and make you feel like you've got thirty seconds to work out how to impress them. I wouldn't mind if they were all witty supermodels with ridiculously high IQs but it's far from it. As most bars and clubs are packed with blokes, even right horror bags with zero personality know they can afford to pick and choose. I don't help myself in those situations either, 'cos I ridiculously assume that if I find a woman physically attractive then they're automatically gonna be humorous and intelligent as well. You'd think after the umpteenth time of standing with some girl, bored out of my skull, it'd sink in that the traits of beauty, wit and intelligence don't necessarily go hand in hand.

I remember one of the first times I approached a girl with the intention of sweeping her off her feet. I'd been out with Kev, as usual, in this terrible club that we always went to called 42nd Street. After successfully negotiating the bouncers and paying the entrance fee, you had to climb a winding stairway and cross a corridor towards three inter-connecting rooms. The first had this circular bar in the middle of the room; the second had the DJ and the dance floor; and the third had chairs and tables in. They were all in a row so you could walk straight though and we'd often do a few laps of the place looking for any women that looked remotely approachable.

The music was this dreadful mix of hip-hop and soul but I really didn't know any different in those days. I absolutely love music now, but back then I didn't have a clue. Unfortunately, I'm one of those pathetic snobs that will like a singer or band right the way up until that singer or band starts getting popular, and then I'll despise them. I guess the way I saw it was that I couldn't stand ninety-nine per cent of the population, so if I thought for a minute that something I liked was popular then it meant I had something in common with people I abhorred. I'm not as bad these days, but I still really don't like it when someone I dislike enjoys something that I like. It doesn't make any sense, I know.

In the last year or two, I've been getting quite obsessive over a lot of sixties girl group stuff and great female vocalists that encompass that kind of sound. Stuff like The Shangri-Las, The Ronettes, The Angels, Lesley Gore, Dusty Springfield – all that kind of thing. Those songs cover the full gamut of emotions, from the defiance bellowed out in The Shangri-Las 'Never Again' and 'You Don't Own Me' by Lesley Gore to the heart wrenching, pathetic pleas on songs such as 'You Don't Love Me No More' by Madeline Bell or 'You Just Have to Say The Word' by Françoise Hardy. There's plenty of humour in some of those songs too. Like in Billie Davis' 'Suffer', for example. That song is addressed to some old flame of hers, who was a bit of a bastard, by all accounts. In the song, she's rejoicing in the fact that he's now pining for her. When his friends tell her he's miserable without her and that he plays their favourite record all the time, she retorts "well when yours wears out, I'll send you mine." *Go girl*.

There's some great lyrics in those songs. I've already made a mental note to religiously play 'Sweet Talkin' Guy' by The Chiffons to my daughter as soon as she nears her teenage years, 'cos the last thing I want is for her to meet some bastard just out for what he can get. I get a real buzz out of discovering some great tune if it's an obscure track that I've never heard before. I just heard this song recently by Reparata & the Delrons called 'Look in My Diary'. It wasn't even released at the time and has just been tagged onto the end of a compilation but I swear, it's a brilliant track. There's loads of stuff once you start looking. I really love it.

It's pretty fucking cringe-worthy thinking how I used to dance like a bastard after one too many half a ciders in that horrible club. I'm really not built for dancing. I've got this long, gangly frame and I feel uncomfortable just standing around, let alone trying to put some rhythmic dance moves together. Anyway, this one particular night I'd spotted a girl that I quite liked the look of. She was sat all the way across the other side of the club and I made the mistake of telling Kevin about it. Now, there's a fine line between constructive encouragement and emotional blackmail and he pretty much crossed it all the time. He'd start out quite relaxed by saying that I should get across and ask her out. As the minutes ticked by, he'd move on to say that if I didn't I might regret it forever and that she could be my future wife and that I should think about how bad I'd feel in the morning if I still didn't know if that girl liked me or not. He had good intentions but after twenty minutes of this incessant 'encouragement', I felt that if I didn't do as he'd suggested that I'd be letting him, my family and the whole *bleeding* world down.

After a verbal battering, and the muddying of reality caused by that disgusting cider, I set off towards her. It felt like I was stood in front of her in the blink of an eye. She was sat on this cushioned chair with her back against a wall. She didn't look as great close up, but there was no turning back at that point. I stood there without saying a word until she looked up at me with this vacant expression across her face. Let's put it this way, she didn't look too fucking overjoyed to see me. Immediately, I realised I should have done a bit more preparation on my romantic approach.

I remember I just stood there sweating for a few seconds as she stared up at me. All of a sudden, I felt *completely* sober.

"Err … Do you want a drink?"

She shook her head. I looked about, unsure what I was supposed to do next. I was pretty fucking frozen with fear, I can tell you.

"Err … Do you want a dance?"

She shook her head again. That was it. I'd used all

my best lines and she'd still not cracked. I immediately turned and walked all the way across the club, back to where Kevin was stood. That walk back seemed to take forever.

"What happened?"

He didn't know *exactly* what had happened, but I think he had a pretty fucking good idea it hadn't gone too well again.

Chapter Twelve

I left that terrible school with a modest haul of qualifications and even less confidence than I started with. Like I said before, I never really pushed myself and I only ever put in the requisite amount of effort that I thought would be required. I ended up going to college, and then university, but for all the wrong reasons. I guess I just thought it was what you were supposed to do, and what I thought my dad expected of me. The main reason though was due to the fact I didn't have a clue what I wanted to do with my life. I guess I felt like it was just prolonging the big decision that I'd have to make one day. I kept thinking that it would suddenly just come to me or, even better, that somebody would make the decision for me. Nothing really filled me with inspiration, nothing that paid good money anyhow. I sure as hell wasn't gonna end up in the family business, and Office Temp or Meat Packer or Shelf Stacker – well, that was about as glamorous as vacancies got in the job centres in Manchester. Sure it would have been great to be a pop star or a footballer but those kinds of jobs require a bit of drive and determination and I've always been completely lacking in either of those attributes. Apathy though is something I have in bleeding bucket loads.

I could have stayed on at Sixth Form at that school in Oldham rather than go to college but, to be honest,

I couldn't wait to get away from that dreary place. I never felt like I belonged the entire time I was there. I desperately wanted to go and find something else although I wasn't entirely sure what it was I was looking for. By that stage in my life, I'd realised that the majority of people I would meet in life would be complete bores or absolute fucking idiots, and I guess I thought that moving to a different place in a different town might increase the possibility of meeting someone I might actually have *something* in common with. Some fucking hope.

It's a difficult time being a teenager. When I look at teenagers now, they pretty much make me puke and I shudder when I think that I used to be one. They no longer exhibit all the naivety and innocence that make children so likeable and they're still a world away from possessing the mental and physical maturities of adulthood. They're full of hormones, attitude and spots. I was no different from most teenagers in that I had an awful haircut and wore some ridiculous clothes in the mistaken belief that I looked cool, whilst maintaining a rebellious air about me. *Fuck you, Society – My hair's long and I'm wearing this bright red top with a pointy hood and no-one's gonna stop me.* Unlike most teenagers though, I kept the bad haircut for about five years longer than I should have done.

I spent my initial teenage years at that house in North Manchester with my *beautiful* stepmother and her *beautiful* family. Because we had moved from my dad's shop to that house, it meant I lived a fair distance from any school friends. I didn't know any of the kids in the neighbourhood and, to be honest, I really didn't want to. Besides, no fucker would have wanted to make friends anyway after the Captain X incident. I told you it was a pretty rough area; a fact that was proven quite appositely one day when my dad's car was stolen and it later transpired that the perpetrators lived across the road from us. I was obviously ecstatic to see the back of it, but the worst part was they didn't even have the decency to write the car off or leave it burnt out in a field. To my utter dismay, it was found and returned to us by the police a few days later.

The upshot of living in such an undesirable area was that I'd usually spend most evenings in that house, only going out if it was my turn to walk the dog. Following the nightly struggle with my tea, I'd go to my room and listen to music, or else have a romantic evening in with one of those magazines. The alternate option was to sit with my step mum and watch whatever *she* decided we would watch on TV. Occasionally, if she was out, I'd try and watch a documentary or a football match or something, but as soon as she'd come back in she'd say 'We're not watching this' and turn the channel over. Even if there was nothing else on that she wanted to watch. She'd just leave it on another channel from the one I was watching. *Fucking charming*. And if we were ever watching anything that looked like being *remotely* interesting then she'd turn the fucker over.

We had to go to bed at nine on a school night and would usually be allowed to stay up a bit later at the weekend. I remember one Saturday night, we were watching that film, *Private Benjamin* with Goldie Hawn. Anyway, we'd been watching for about an hour or so when all of a sudden the action got a bit steamy and it looked like we were gonna get to see Private Benjamin's privates. The film had been pretty lousy up to that point but when you've watched something for an hour then you wanna see what happens in the end, and you definitely wanna see any saucy bits. My step mum was having none of it though and just as Goldie started getting passionate then my step mum announced that the film was rubbish and turned the fucking TV over. I dunno if she thought she was protecting us from somehow being corrupted by that tame simulated sex scene but, ironically, her actions forced me to go upstairs and study my big books of breasts and vaginas.

It's so crazy how uptight people are about sex and how worked up people get about the naked body, in this country anyway. Even after the watershed, when all kids are supposed to be in bed, you won't get the slightest complaint about extreme violence but a hint of nudity has the nation dashing for the phone. It cracks me up when they show people naked and then pixellate their privates as though the sight of a penis or vagina is gonna somehow corrupt all the watching adults. *I mean, who the fuck gets offended by seeing a naked body?* I'm offended we *don't* get to see more people on TV naked. Occasionally, you'll get to see bare knockers or arses and *very* occasionally you'll get to see a dick. Only flaccid ones mind; even in the year two thousand and nine the sight of an erect penis is obviously a threat to national security.

I can never understand for the life of me why people get so worked up about 'bad language' either. You've probably noticed by now that I utter the *occasional* swear word and I'm not gonna try to say it's big or clever to curse. I normally just use it to emphasise what it is I'm saying, and maybe it just masks a limited vocabulary on my part, but for fuck's sake, in the big scheme of things it's just an amalgamation of letters that for, whatever reason, somebody at some stage in history has decided isn't the most appropriate thing to utter. In a world where immense suffering and cruelty is rife; where wars and conflict rage; where emotional, physical and mental torture is inflicted on millions, how can anyone summon the energy to get worked up about something so insignificantly unimportant as swearing? In my opinion, *Coronation Street* would be a lot more interesting with an injection of foul language. And erect penises. I'll write to *Points of View*.

I told you earlier that my bedroom was adjacent to the room my sister shared with my stepsister. Well, my bed was against the adjoining wall and there was a gap near the bedstead where a radiator sat between both rooms. It had originally been one big room before my dad separated it into two with a partitioning wall. My stepsister slept on the opposite side of the wall to my bed and she'd often chat with me after lights out when we'd been instructed to go to sleep. We talked about all kinds of stuff and it was her that first told me about sex. I couldn't believe it at the time. It sounds bleeding disgusting when you're a kid, and I couldn't envisage for a second that some of the parents of the kids at school would do something like *that*. Now I'm older, I realise there's not much else to life than trying to make the most of simple pleasures, like sex.

Sex was pretty much a taboo subject in our household. My dad never broached the topic with us and quite frankly I was more than happy about that. Obviously it would have been handy to know all that stuff, but my dad was the last person on Earth I would have wanted to explain it all. My mum was relatively more open about that kind of thing but I'd have died of embarrassment if either of them had mentioned anything about that particular topic. That reminds me of a time years ago at my mum's house. My mate had come round and everyone was sat about watching TV in the living room. We used to play this game during the commercial breaks where we'd see who could be the first one to recognise the advert and shout out the answer. This is what passed for entertainment for teenagers back in the day before PlayStation arrived. Our game got quite competitive and I was eager to beat my pal. In the midst of one particular game, a commercial came on that I'm sure you'd recognise. It was the one with the cute puppy and the toilet paper. I was in like a flash.

"DUREX!"

As soon as the word left my mouth, I realised my mistake and felt the blood rush to my cheeks. It was an easy mistake to say Durex instead of Andrex but confusing a toilet paper manufacturer with a condom manufacturer was incredibly embarrassing to my teenage self. My bastard friend was doubled-up in hysterics. I continued to stare straight ahead at the television set. I couldn't look at my mum. She was really cool about it and said that I shouldn't be embarrassed as it was good that I knew about contraception. It just made me feel worse though and it was probably at least ten minutes before my good friend stopped sniggering and I was able to look away from the TV screen. So you see there was no way I was gonna learn about sex from my mum and dad and it was left to my school friends and step sister to educate me.

My step sister used to tell me all sorts of stuff between the radiator gap, and most of it was pretty dull. I remember one night we'd been chatting for a bit and she said she had a funny joke to tell me. It was something about two prostitutes talking and one says that she can smell semen and the other one says it's because she's just belched. I didn't laugh or anything, partly because it was fucking rubbish, but partly 'cos I was a bit embarrassed. The next second though, my bedroom door was flung open and my dad stormed in and grabbed me by the arm and pulled me out of bed. My eyes were half-closed as they struggled to adjust to the bright light streaming in from the landing. My dad wasn't too pleased and he roared at me.

"If you don't want to go to sleep, then you can come and sit downstairs."

As I was ushered down the stairs in my pyjamas, I once again felt hard done by. *She* was the one who had been doing all the talking and yet it was *me* getting dragged downstairs. My step mum was sat watching TV and my dad poked me towards the armchair furthest away near the wall.

"You can stay up all night if you don't want to go to sleep."

In my opinion it was a fucking overreaction on his part, but he didn't look in any mood to want to debate the issue. Besides, the only thing that was in my mind was that he must have heard the dirty joke she told, and that made me feel incredibly embarrassed. I really didn't like the idea that my dad thought I indulged in sperm related humour. I wanted to tell him that I thought it was pretty crude and totally unfunny, but if he hadn't heard it properly then he might have made me tell the joke again. I really had no inclination to do spunk gags in front of him and my step mum.

I can recall after a while that my eyelids began to droop and I'd start dropping off, but every time I did he'd poke me with his bony finger and tell me that I could have gone to sleep before, and that I obviously didn't want to. It might technically have been classed as child abuse, and was definitely on a par with methods used in Guantanamo Bay, but those sleep deprivation tactics worked a treat. I was finally allowed to go to bed when they went up and I sure as fuck didn't talk after lights out again.

It wasn't miserable the *whole* time we were in that house. Occasionally, and I remember it would usually be Friday evenings, our step mum would decide she'd fancy some supper, and dispatch one of her kids to the chippy. We'd be allowed a portion of chips each and it was always a great experience tearing open the chip paper as the pungent aroma of vinegar filled your nostrils and your mouth began to salivate in anticipation of the greasy meal ahead. The last of the chips would usually be drenched in vinegar and stuck to the greaseproof paper and I'd have to peel it away before savouring the last mouthful. I know a plateful of chips doesn't seem much to get excited about but, believe you me, it was like ambrosia from the gods compared to that microwaved crap we had to stomach most days.

I remember we were all really pleased the day my dad brought that dog home that I told you about. It was apparently a cross between a Labrador and an Alsatian. It was some kind of mongrel anyway. It had this yellowy-golden coat, shiny black eyes and a big wet nose. It was a bit of a lively fucker and I remember it was prancing all over the place and jumping up at everyone when it arrived. It's crazy the way that dogs are so excitable and get so worked up when they see you. I reckon its nice getting that affectionate response every time you get home though. I doubt whether my step mum, in her entire fucking life, had *ever* had an enthusiastic response when walking into a room before.

My step sister was allowed to choose the dog's name, which me and my sister were a bit pissed off about. Now I don't know about you, but I think you need to give it a lot of thought when choosing a dog's name. You should consider the fact that, on a regular occasion, you're gonna have to wail that name really loudly in public, when you're trying to get the fucker back on his lead. She obviously didn't consider this fact at *all* though. She came up with the name 'Karma'. The rationale behind the dog's name wasn't – as you might be thinking – a nod to my step sister's spiritual beliefs as a devout aficionado of some Indian religion. The name originated from her affection for the pop group Culture Club. Instead of going for the obvious moniker of the lead singer 'George', she instead took her inspiration from the title of one of their insipid hit singles, 'Karma Chameleon'. If you're sat there thinking that it isn't *that* bad a name for a dog, then *you* try shouting 'Karma' incessantly for twenty minutes in the middle of Boggart Hole Clough without feeling like a complete dick.

The only other real fond memories I have of being in that house with her family, were all around Christmas time. I really enjoy Christmas. I always have done. I'm not remotely religious or anything, but I've always looked forward to that particular time of the year. My mum must have hated it though. Me and my sister weren't exactly sympathetic to our mother's wretched financial situation and each Christmas we'd mither her until she gave into our unreasonable demands. We both knew full well that my dad wouldn't splash out on the expensive gifts we'd often crave and therefore we'd end up asking my mum. The only income she had consisted of the paltry amount she received in state benefits and she *really* wasn't in any position to be able to start wasting cash on extravagant presents for us. She always managed to get us what we'd asked for though and I guess it's 'cos she felt giving us those presents might make up for her own perceived deficiencies as a mother. She probably carried a lot of guilt around with her when it came to her kids, what with her having to leave us with our dad and spend a lot of time away from us in hospital.

We never gave it any thought at the time but the only way she was able to afford our presents was by getting into debt. She'd usually get us stuff from shopping catalogues which meant she'd be able to pay for items in instalments. It also meant it would be another three fucking Christmases' before she'd finish paying for the pool table I harangued her for. The only other way she could afford to get her demanding offspring expensive gifts would be to borrow off local moneylenders. These cunts would make a small fortune exploiting vulnerable, poverty-stricken people by offering up-front loans at extortionate rates of interest. I remember on several occasions that the doorbell would ring and my mum would instruct me to hide behind the sofa and not make a sound because she didn't have the money to repay when the loan sharks came calling. Debt can be a heavy fucking millstone around someone's neck and it was the last thing that somebody already suffering from depression needed. I know for a fact that one of the reasons she got into debt was because of us and I also know for a fact that being in debt caused her a lot of worry. Indirectly we worsened her depression which pushed her to feel she didn't want to live anymore. You don't think about these things when you're a kid though. I'd make sure she never had to worry about money again if she was still here. But she isn't.

Obviously, I loved receiving presents as a kid at Christmas, but there were also other little things that made the whole season enjoyable for me too. That house with my step family was a miserable place to live in for the majority of the time, but for a couple of weeks at the end of each year, it used to somehow seem a nicer place to be. I know it was still inhabited by her and her awful family, and I know the only real difference to the house was just a crappy Christmas tree covered in cheap lights and walls decorated in garish tinsel, but somehow it made it all a bit more bearable for that short period of time.

I remember I used to enjoy poring over the bumper Christmas editions of the *TV Times* and the *Radio Times* and mentally making a note of all the programmes and films on TV I wanted to watch. Not that I'd have a fucking chance of watching them, mind. There was absolutely no chance of her relinquishing that remote control. I used to love TV at Christmas when I was a kid, though. Everything would change for that holiday fortnight. All the usual shows had their own Christmas specials and there used to be loads more movies and cartoons on. Even the titles between shows would change for the better, like for example when they'd show the Granada TV ident with snow over the tops of the letters.

One thing that would always get me though, was when they'd have these sanitised news broadcasts on Christmas Day. The television news on Christmas Day is always really short and usually just mentions what the Queen was waffling on about in her speech. It's like the broadcasters think that they'd best pretend that there's no crime in case it ruins anyone's special, family day. When I was younger, I always watched those Christmas Day news broadcasts and I'd actually tell myself that the entire criminal fraternity had all agreed that December 25th was off limits. Well, I can tell you all from bitter experience that it's a big cover up by the TV broadcasters. Even on Christmas Day, the world is still full of thieving bastards.

I used to have this great bicycle when I was younger. It was a Raleigh Spider and it was all yellow with black mudguards and black painted webbing all over the frame. I didn't really have any friends outside of school in those days. Don't feel sorry for me or anything though, 'cos I quite liked being on my own and I remember I used to spend most Saturday mornings riding that bike up and down the roads that surrounded my dad's shop.

There used to be this American cop show called *CHiPs* on TV at the time, starring these two police motorcyclists called Jon and Ponch. I think Ponch got his name from his surname, which was Poncherello or something. I wasn't as keen on him though and usually sided with the more exotically named Jon. It was called *CHiPs* 'cos it was about the Californian Highway Patrol (I don't think the 'i' and the 's' stood for anything). Every Saturday morning I used to pretend to be Jon out of *CHiPs*. The side streets of Chadderton became the highways of California and my Raleigh Spider transformed into a Kawasaki 1000.

I used to have some great times racing up and down the Californian highways of Oldham. Anyway, the reason I'm telling you about that bike is because some fucker stole it from the yard at the side of my dad's shop. And not only did they fucking steal it but they decided to steal it on Christmas morning. *Christmas fucking morning!* I ended up getting a second hand BMX for my birthday to replace it, but it wasn't the same and I had to admit my days in the Californian Highway Patrol were numbered.

As soon as I reached the grand old age of sixteen and left school, then I moved in with my mum and left The Addams Family behind. I felt a little bad about leaving my sister behind but there was no way my dad would have allowed her to move to my mum's house until she'd finished school. I think my mum was happy to have me there but, to be honest, I didn't really consult her and she probably felt obliged to let me stay after not being able to have us full time for all those years. Looking back, I was probably a drain on her already meagre finances, what with me going to college and not earning a wage to help out. If I could go back in time then I definitely would have got a job to help out with things, rather than go to college and university.

Her depression never really went away and she was pretty up and down for the whole time I was living there. She was on a lot of medication, although I didn't have a clue what it was for. I think they didn't have too much of a clue how to treat it and so just kept plying her with different combinations of 'happy pills'. I didn't pay much attention really, 'cos I was too busy tied up with being a teenager and worrying about my own vitally important agenda, which comprised entirely of trying to meet girls.

I finally got lucky one Saturday night, at that terrible 42nd Street club that I told you about. I say got lucky, but she wasn't all that great looking if you must know, but hey, it was a start. The only reason I'd got talking to her was because I'd been stood next to her and, unlike most of the girls in there, she'd actually seemed happy to chat to me. That fact alone should really have put me off her. I guess her standards must have been as low as mine. I can't even remember what I talked to her about but it would have been complete inane drivel 'cos all I was thinking about was how I was going to go about trying to get my first kiss. It was at that moment that I invented this technique that stood me in pretty good stead for the rest of my teenage days.

What I'd do was gently brush her hand with mine whilst we were chatting, as though it was accidental. If she didn't pull away from that contact, and the conversation was going okay, then I'd gently take a hold of her hand. If she still didn't break away, then I knew the green light was on and I could move in for a kiss. It's all down to the confidence thing and me having to be pretty fucking certain that they were gonna respond positively to my advances. Rejection is a killer.

Anyway, that first time I'd held her hand and I was telling myself that I had to go in for the kiss. At the next break in conversation, I moved in and sought out her lips with mine. To be quite honest, I didn't have a fucking clue what I was doing. Her tongue seemed to come out of nowhere and I didn't know how the fuck to react apart from to just stick mine out too. It was quite awkward and we had numerous attempts but none of them were that great and I got pretty stressed every time she went in for the kill. I was glad to break my duck though and there was a tangible sense of relief on my part.

In those days I thought it was only right to start seeing someone if they'd let you kiss them and, besides, there was always the chance that kissing would develop into other stuff. I saw that girl for about a month or so and met her a couple of times a week. I'd known from the start that, even though she was a nice girl and all, I wasn't that attracted to her and it pretty much just fizzled out in the end. The worst part was that I didn't even get much further than the kissing, although that did begin to get more enjoyable. We did spend a night together though and I really had my hopes up that it might be *the* night.

We'd gone to a party for a friend of hers in Blackburn and we'd been invited to stay over. Throughout the evening, I kept subtly yawning as I was desperately eager for us to get to bed. When we *did* finally retire for the night, I was incredibly nervous as I suddenly realised I wasn't too sure about what I was going to have to do. My entire sex education to date had comprised of the odd ill-informed line from my step sister and the content of the reader's letters pages from *Razzle* magazine. Apart from those magazines, I'd only ever seen one woman naked before in my life and that was my seventeen year old step sister, so I don't even think that counted.

I remember I'd come home from school one day and I'd been dying for a wee. I'd bounded up the stairs, pressed the handle down on the bathroom door and flung it open. My step sister was stood in the middle of the bathroom floor, totally naked with a bath towel in her hand. It was probably more of a shock for me than it was for her. The strange thing was that she made no attempt to cover herself up at all. I don't know whether it was because it happened so fast, or whether she just felt sorry for me and let me have a gander 'cos she thought I was unlikely to ever get to see another woman naked. I automatically went back out and shut the door behind me. In an attempt to overcome my embarrassment, I shouted something like 'You should have locked the door', although really I wanted to shout 'Can I have another look?'

Back in that small bedroom in that strange house

in Blackburn, we both began to get undressed in total silence. The only thing that was keeping me from shrieking and exiting by the nearest window was the thought that she was probably even more worried than I was. I avoided looking across at where she was getting changed to spare her any embarrassment. I also still couldn't believe the fact that a woman was agreeing to get into bed with me. I was half-expecting she might come to her senses any moment, suddenly shriek 'Pervert!' and ring the local constabulary. I climbed tentatively under the duvet, dressed provocatively in a worn t-shirt with the logo of a band across the front and a pair of bright blue Bermuda shorts. She climbed into bed beside me dressed in a pale blue Minnie Mouse nightie. I'd never seen any of the women in those magazines with that particular outfit on. I must admit, it's pretty difficult to think passionate thoughts when you've got a cartoon mouse in a big polka dot pink bow, staring back at you. Maybe that's what she'd planned though, 'cos by the end of the night I was still the big virgin I'd started out as.

We'd started kissing and I'd let my hands wander but, to be honest, I was pretty glad when she'd stop me 'cos I wasn't exactly too sure what to do if I'd have got to where they were wandering. To tell you the truth, I was happy just lying there kissing, but I felt like she'd think there was something wrong with me if I *didn't* try it on with her. About two hours later, she finally removed her nightie and bra whilst telling me that she wouldn't 'take her top off for just anyone.' I dunno whether by saying that, she thought I'd feel special or something, but in all honesty I wasn't fussed whether she'd flashed them at the bus driver that morning, I just wanted a look. It was all a bit of an anti-climax in the end really and I was just happy in the knowledge that someone could remove their bra without me ejaculating all over the place.

Chapter Thirteen

Manchester was a great place to be in the late nineteen-eighties / early nineteen-nineties. Through friends and people I'd met at college, I'd started to discover decent music and there were loads of excellent local bands to see in concert, like The Fall, The Stone Roses, Man from Delmonte and James. I'd also begun to listen to The Smiths and The Chameleons, although both those groups had recently split up. In my view they're the greatest bands to come out of Manchester and they remain two of my favourites. There were some cool clubs and bars to go to back then such as Devilles, The Venue, Corbieres, and The Haçienda. They'd play all that music plus a load of classic stuff by bands such as The Doors, The Mamas and the Papas and The Beatles. It's still a thrill to imagine walking down the stairs to The Venue and hearing the loud, reverberating drums of 'What's the World'; racing down The Brickhouse staircase to reach the dance floor for 'In Shreds'; or dancing around the cavernous Haçienda to 'I Wanna be your Dog'. By dancing, I mean we'd usually walk slowly around the dance floor whilst nodding our heads to the tune. John Travolta wouldn't last a fucking minute in Devilles with his convoluted repertoire.

I'd buy tonnes of vinyl from Piccadilly Records and Vinyl Exchange, which were two great record shops in Manchester. I used to love going in and browsing for ages and I'd regularly buy stuff I'd never even heard of before. Most of it would be terrible, but it would all be worthwhile if I happened to discover some great song or band. In those days, I'd go out at night quite a lot, although fuck knows how I used to be able to afford it. I didn't spend that much time at home and when I did I'd usually just stay in my room and listen to music or play computer games. I suppose most teenagers are pretty much the same in that respect. I've always loved computer games but, as an adult, it's not the done thing to admit to, and the social stigma is pretty much on a par with paedophilia and bestiality. I really don't get it 'cos it's just a slice of escapism as far as I'm concerned, like watching a film or reading a book. It's a lot more civilised than supposed '*adult*' pursuits, such as having sex or getting blind drunk.

My bedroom at my mum's house was quite small with just enough room for a single bed and a little table which held a portable TV. My walls would usually be adorned with football memorabilia or posters of whichever band or singers I was into at the time. I must have been eight or nine when I first started getting into music and I distinctly remember watching *Top of the Pops* and having the strange feelings for Kim Wilde that I had had for Miss Hill (I still can't bring myself to call her 'Mrs Carter'). I bought her first single, 'Kids in America', from Woolworths one weekend when I was in town with my mum. I played the record incessantly once I got home and belted out the chorus with greater gusto each time.

"*We're the kids in America*

WOAH!

Everybody lives for the music go round"

I didn't have a clue what the fuck she was going on about, but as I stared intently at her picture on the record sleeve and sang, this eight year old Mancunian *was* a kid in America for those three minutes and twenty-six seconds.

Although the purchase of that record was *slightly* influenced by Kim Wilde's sultry performance on *Top of the Pops*, the song itself was a decent enough pop tune. I couldn't say the same about my purchases of Belinda Carlisle's records during my early teens. I had a huge poster of her on my wall at one stage, in that small bedroom at my mum's house. I remember it covered an entire wall and was adjacent to a poster of Sherilyn Fenn from the TV series *Twin Peaks*, another celebrity my adolescent mind was lusting over at the time. In the poster, Belinda Carlisle was wearing this low cut, green satin dress and the angle the picture had been taken at showed off an impressive cleavage. I don't think I was fooling anyone that the poster was a symbol of my appreciation of 'Heaven Is a Place on Earth'. It was pretty obvious it was more a symbol of my appreciation of big knockers.

The only downside of moving away from my step mum was the fact I no longer had any access to my step brother's mountain of pornography. I had gotten used to my masturbating routine and I realised I was gonna have to use my initiative from that moment forward. The poster of Belinda sufficed for a while, as did pictures within various other magazines. The search for masturbatory material was a constant struggle and I'll give you an idea of the depths I had to sink to.

I just told you I was into computer games and most boys either had a ZX Spectrum or Commodore 64 during my schooldays. My computer of choice was the Spectrum. I say 'choice' although it looked for a long time as though I'd have no fucking chance of getting either machine. I'd wanted a Spectrum for ages and my dad finally agreed to buy me one about four hundred years after they first came out. Not a new one mind. I got a second-hand one off some guy that had put an advertisement in the local paper. It was pretty cheap but my dad still haggled with the poor bastard and got the price down even lower. It only came with a couple of games but that wasn't a problem because cassette tapes full of pirated games were constantly circulating the classroom. One of the games on those cassette tapes was the all-time classic *Samantha Fox Strip Poker*. Before you say anything, I appreciate that discussing this particular 'game' isn't *that* helpful towards my crusade to make computer gaming become socially acceptable as an adult pursuit.

You gotta remember that the graphics in computer games back then weren't the best. I'm no pornography snob though and I was certain those digitised photos of Sam Fox would be sufficient for my requirements. I knew I'd only have to win a few hands of poker in order to get her kit off and feast my eyes on those grainy pictures. Unfortunately, there were two *small* issues. Firstly, I didn't have a fucking clue how to play poker. Secondly, I didn't have a copy of the instruction booklet that would no doubt have accompanied the retail version of the game. Not to fear, I thought – I was sure I'd get the hang of it quickly enough. I was certain getting her down to her bra would provide ample visual stimulus for me. Besides, she got her knockers out for a living – my teenage mind decided she mustn't be *that* bright. I figured my mental capacity would be more than sufficient to get her naked in minutes. I loaded up the game with my trousers around my ankles.

Any chance of some quick relief disappeared when I saw the first black and white computer image of Sam. Any thoughts of her commencing proceedings in some sexy, skimpy outfit were immediately quashed. Not only was she dressed in a large, winter coat, but she was also wearing a fedora, a pair of dark glasses and a big, striped scarf. I was sat there with my genitals already on display before a card had been dealt. That cheating bitch had turned up dressed as Dr. *fucking* Who.

I won a couple of rounds, without knowing what I was doing, and yet she didn't take a stitch off. I imagined those game developers sat back in their chairs laughing at the thousands of disappointed adolescents sat half-naked with tissues at the ready. Unfortunately I couldn't take my pirated copy back to Woolworths to complain, and I knew *Watchdog* was unlikely to take up the case of a frustrated teenage pervert.

I stuck at that game and eventually managed to play a decent enough hand to see a few digitised photos of her without the coat, although I remember they weren't *that* much more stimulating than the first one. When I look back though, the experience of that game did have *one* positive influence on my life. Nowadays, you're forever hearing women moan about the fact that guys aren't romantic enough. I can bet my life that those guys never played *Samantha Fox Strip Poker*. Having to splash out on the odd gift and fancy meal is *nothing* compared to becoming a fucking grandmaster at poker in order to see them in their underwear.

I barely spoke to my mum and used to just spend most of my time in my room. Throughout my life, I never spent much time chatting to her, or any of my family come to think of it. It wasn't that I didn't like them or anything, it's just that I've never been good at small talk and I felt like I didn't have anything much to say. I'd just ask whether they were ok and make some general chit-chat about something or other for a couple of minutes. I guess I've never been much of a talker, especially where my family are concerned and I've never felt I've had *that* much in common with them. I like my own company and I can't really see the point of saying anything to anybody unless it's genuinely of some interest. Like I said, throughout my life, people have wrongly interpreted it as me being 'quiet', or even 'ignorant', but it basically boils down to the fact that I can't be arsed joining in people's conversations, or talking for talking's sake.

I try my best to avoid any kind of social gatherings where there's gonna be a chance I might have to talk to someone new. The worst instances I've experienced are when girlfriends have insisted on us attending the homes of their friends for dinner or some other kind of social function. I remember this one time when one girlfriend had arranged for us to go and spend the evening at a friend of hers and her boyfriend. I only agreed to go 'cos I knew she'd be really mad if I didn't, but I remember I was pretty much dreading the whole thing.

Those kind of evenings don't make the *slightest* bit of sense to me. Just because you've got a girlfriend, why the *fuck* do they think you'll want to spend the evening with one of their friends and their friend's boyfriend? I didn't particularly enjoy spending too much time with some of the girlfriends I've had, let alone with their friends and their friend's boyfriends. When you have a girlfriend though, you have to put up with meeting their friends and their parents, and attending all kinds of things that are just unbearable. You have to make an *awful* lot of concessions when you're in a relationship.

This one time, I remember I was feeling sorry for her friend's boyfriend before I'd even walked through the door. We got to their house and exchanged pleasantries and all, and then her friend took my girlfriend off to show her around the house, so I was left with the boyfriend. I did try, but I told you I *really* find it difficult. What can I say? I'm a bleeding weirdo.

"So how long have you two been together?"

Now don't try and tell me for one fucking minute that he really wanted to know the answer to that fucking question. Like I said, it's just talking for the *sake* of talking. If I'd have had any balls, I'd have just responded the truthful way and saved us a lot of energy and discomfort.

"Look, neither of us wants to be here, and the only reason we *are* here is just to please our girlfriends. We've not really got anything in common with our girlfriends and we're unlikely to have anything in common with each other. Neither of us gives a fuck about where the other lives; what job we do; or how long we've been with our girlfriends. Let's put our heads together and come up with an excuse to cut this evening short before I get that bored I resort to blowing my brains out, with a shotgun, all over your new kitchen."

That's what I wanted to say. But I didn't.

"About two years. What about you and ….?

I couldn't remember her name. Or his name. To be fair to him, he kept trying, but he was fighting a losing battle. I wasn't trying to be ignorant or anything, I just really struggle in those forced situations.

My girlfriend was obviously not too happy with me. I think she expected me to conduct a charm offensive and regale them all with witty anecdotes. Instead I just sat there, uttering the occasional word, and nodding. The nodding, combined with an '*I'm listening intently to what you're saying*' look was part of my highly elaborate plan to delude them into believing I was lapping up their conversation. It didn't work though. My girlfriend wouldn't speak to me on the way home and they both probably thought I was a right ignorant bastard. I apologised to her although, obviously, I didn't mean it.

Chapter Fourteen

There was a gang of us that used to go to those cool bars and clubs in the centre of town that I mentioned earlier. I've already told you about Kevin and another of them – a guy called Simon – is great and remains a close friend. I knew the others through Kevin and, to be quite frank, I wished I didn't. They weren't particularly the kind of people I wanted to spend any time with and I think the feeling was mutual. It wasn't that they were all horrible individuals or anything. I mean, a couple of them were really nice and pleasant and all, but they were deathly dull and weren't the kind of guys you'd wanna be stuck in a lift with.

Although we all used to go out together, I'd only consider Kev and Simon to be *actual* bona fide friends. As I've intimated, I'm not *exactly* a people person, and I only really like people who have something about them, or something interesting to say. I'd much rather have a small close knit bunch of mates than a big group of bland acquaintances. Kevin and Simon, for example, are people that have something about them.

I'll tell you this tale about Kev that might give you an idea of just what kind of person he is. When I first met him, he lived in a terraced house a few doors down from my mum. There were quite a few kids that lived in and around that street and let's just say that he didn't exactly get on with all of them. In fact, it's probably fair to say that some of those kids pretty much hated him. To be honest, there were a fair few days when even *I* did 'cos he could be a bit of a bastard at times. His heart is in the right place though and you couldn't ask for more loyal a pal. Anyway, this one time we'd been walking through the alleyway at the bottom of those terraced houses when we spotted a freshly-daubed piece of graffiti across the end wall. In white painted letters, no more than a few inches high, someone had made the following statement:

"KJ IS A DICK"

What with those being Kev's initials, and with the graffiti being so close to his house, it was apparent to all that he was the subject of the proclamation. Kev didn't show any obvious displeasure but it soon became apparent that he wasn't too happy with the message and his brain was sent whirring into action. His response to the graffiti shows what a fucking crazy mind he possesses and why he has that certain something about him. Now, I'm pretty sure that most recipients who'd had vandalism of that nature directed at them would have either just ignored it (being that it didn't actually spell out his name), or maybe attempted to clean it off or paint over it. Not Kevin. His solution was a bit more unorthodox. The next day, anybody walking past the same wall would see the graffiti amended thus:

"KJ IS A DICK TURPIN"

Seriously, what kind of twisted, fucked-up mind would think to get some *Tipp-ex* correction fluid and painstakingly make that kind of amendment? Crazy. That tale kind of sums of up why I love him though.

We spent quite a lot of time at each other's houses as Kevin was so close by. He lived with his mum, dad and older brother, although his brother didn't seem to be around that much. His mum was a sweet, little old Irish woman who was always really welcoming and you honestly couldn't wish to meet a nicer person. The warm reception I felt from his mum was in sharp contrast to the fear that struck me anytime I happened to meet his dad. I used to be incredibly shy around people I didn't really know and could feel quite intimidated when faced with any kind of overbearing personalities. In contrast to the soft, lilting southern Irish tone of Kev's mother's voice, his father had a harsh scouse accent that would leave me quaking. He used to reside in a large armchair in front of the TV in the living room. I guess he was ok and I can't really explain why, but I was scared stiff anytime I had to talk to him.

Me and Kevin would often spend time sat in his front room listening to records and chatting. Occasionally our conversation would be interrupted by a shrill cry from the Liverpudlian in the adjoining room. Sometimes he'd tell us to come and join him and we'd usually sit on the couch, barely speaking. One Saturday morning, we were sat on that sofa when Kev's dad began to proudly tell me about the new microwave oven they'd recently bought. He then ventured into the kitchen after announcing he was gonna make us something to eat and show us the prowess of his new gadget. We both protested that we didn't want anything to eat but he was the sort of guy who wouldn't take no for an answer. He returned about ten minutes later and handed us each a small plate of sandwiches and told us to tuck in. After lifting the top slice of white bread, we were to discover that the new microwave had been used to cook sausages. I am not, and never have been, much of a chef, but I was pretty fucking sure you weren't supposed to cook sausages in a microwave. They definitely didn't *look* cooked anyway. We said thanks and tentatively thumbed the sandwiches eager for the other to take a bite in order to use the resulting scene of vomiting and death as an excuse to pass up the offer. He stared at us from his armchair and repeated his encouragement for us to start eating. I'd immediately noticed that he'd not made any fucking sandwiches for himself.

Kev must have been as terrified of him as I was 'cos he didn't have the courage to protest and there was no way *I* was gonna say anything. The sausages were warm but they still looked pink and raw. If they *had* been in that microwave then I'm not certain he'd plugged the fucker in. They definitely weren't ready to eat and he'd probably have had the same impact by sticking them in his underpants for a few minutes. After further cajoling from his dad, we both took a bite of our sandwich. I really don't know how I managed to do it but I took a few mouthfuls and kept them down despite feeling like I was gonna gag any minute. I'm not sure whether he genuinely thought he'd cooked them, or whether he was bored and wanted to torture us for a laugh before *World of Sport* started. To be fair, he let us off after a few bites and took both plates back in the kitchen. I'm a vegetarian nowadays and I like to think it's due to my caring nature and respect for the animal kingdom but I suspect those fucking sandwiches have got a lot to do with it.

Simon is a totally different kettle of fish to Kevin but he's still one of a kind. An absolute fucking enigma. He's probably the brightest guy I know, and a great person to boot, but he's got a load of idiosyncrasies which crack me up. For example, he always expects his friends to do all the running. You *always* have to ring him, or visit him; like he's doing you a bleeding *favour* by agreeing to be your friend. I swear you could call him every day for six years, without anything in return and if you went a week without ringing him, he'd say 'Oh, not heard from you for a while' as though he'd break out in fucking boils or something if he had to go to the immense trouble of dialling your number. Everyone would ring him though 'cos he's a great listener and so he was the first port of call for any of us that needed to chat something through. He also introduced me to a lot of great music and books. My life would be a lot poorer without having listened to The Chameleons, or having read stuff like *Flowers for Algernon*, and I've got Simon to thank for that.

I can't even remember the names of some of the other guys we used to hang around with. I saw one of them recently in this bar I was in. I swear it must have been the best part of twenty years since I'd last seen him. His name's Jimmy and he was always a really decent, polite guy, but he was also a real bore. I'm not saying I'm some gorgeous bastard or anything but Jimmy was quite an ugly looking guy. It wouldn't have mattered if he'd had the most beautiful face in history though, because on either side of his head he had these large jug ears. Despite the face and the personality and the fucking *huge* ears, he managed to get himself a girlfriend, which we were all pretty amazed and jealous about. She wasn't that bad looking, either. Fair play to the guy 'cos while most of us were inventing stories about girls, he was putting us all to shame with the real thing. Anyway, I feel pretty bad about that night that I saw him again 'cos I deliberately avoided him the entire time. I struggled to hold a conversation with him when we were supposed to be friends, so I knew any attempt at conversation would have been excruciatingly awkward. I don't know if he saw me, or even recognised me, but I sure as fuck recognised those ears. He may have been avoiding speaking to me too, and to be honest, he probably would have gone up in my estimation if he *was* avoiding me, 'cos I always thought he'd be too nice to do something like that.

I think, for the most part anyway, that all the kids in that group were people that Kev and Simon knew through school and so they weren't necessarily close friends or anything. We used to gather at one of their houses each Saturday night and have a few drinks and a few smokes before getting the bus into town. We never went to my mum's house as it was way too small. Besides, my mum would have probably drunk us all under the table. I was never a great drinker back then and I could never really see the attraction of alcohol. I suppose I still can't. I'd also seen the effect it had on my mum and that kind of took away any of the glamour that it might have held for other teenagers. We used to drink cider or lager but it was just a means to get merry on my part, and to instil some Dutch courage for the night ahead.

Alcohol has a pretty devastating effect on certain people, even those that *aren't* alcoholics. Some people get abusive or violent, but even worse than that are those people that get all loud and suddenly think they're the funniest guys on the planet. I hate those fuckers. They're almost as annoying as the people who think they're really cool 'cos they smoke. A few of the group smoked cigarettes, but I could never see the attraction of that either. The smell is disgusting and it always seemed to be a pretty fucking selfish habit for someone to have. I mean, the smokers themselves are getting whatever enjoyment they get out of it, but it's at the expense of every other poor bastard in their vicinity. It's bad enough having to breathe in the obnoxious fumes, let alone having to cop a nice fucking dose of lung cancer to top it all off. *Cheers, you twats*. I'd hate being with a girl that smoked, although obviously I would put up with the foul smell and risk of terminal disease if it meant I might get to sleep with them.

Occasionally, one of the guys would get hold of some weed from somewhere or other. We'd gather in one of the group's bedrooms and each of them would sit around, take a drag and then pass the joint between them. I was the only one who passed up the opportunity and that was pretty fucking ironic, if you ask me, 'cos after listening to some of those boring fuckers for half an hour, *I* was the one who *really* needed some kind of artificial stimulant.

After an hour or so of drinking, smoking and talking crap, we'd usually get the bus into town. On Saturday nights, we'd regularly go to one of those cool clubs I told you about – Devilles. It was split into two large, separate rooms and both played fantastic music. As well as the brilliant music, the drinks were pretty cheap and there were always plenty of girls there too. There was a corridor that connected both rooms with a toilet at each end. All along that corridor was a bench and it used to be frustrating walking to the toilet and seeing lucky bastards kissing and groping girls along the way. Some weekends, I'd have spent the entire week looking forward to going there, only to get turned away by the bouncers on the door for being underage. That was a *right* fucking kick in the balls, I can tell you. Being the close knit, dependable group of pals that we were, everybody would *still* go in the club, even if one of us had been turned away.

One time, me and Kev decided to go to this 'all-nighter' that was taking place at 42nd Street. We'd never been to one before and it seemed quite cool thinking about partying in a club all night before emerging into daylight the following morning. I did have *one* concern about that night though. Namely, that I was usually incapable of drinking more than three halves of cider before spouting utter gibberish and stumbling around. Therefore a whole night of drinking would *surely* kill me. Fortunately there was no way my paltry finances would have allowed me to drink all night long, even if I'd been physically able. I came to the conclusion that the biggest plus of going to that 'all-nighter' was that it would give even someone like me ample time to chat some unfortunate girl up.

I remember there was already a decent sized queue

snaking alongside the club when we got there. I wore a stonewashed denim jacket that I'd borrowed from Kev and I was understandably disappointed there were no audible gasps of excitement from the girls in the queue as we walked past to join the end. When the doors eventually opened, the queue started to inch forward, albeit quite slowly. As we edged nearer to the front it became clear as to the cause of the delay. The bouncers were searching people prior to allowing them to enter. I guessed it was to check that none of the patrons were attempting to smuggle in their own drinks. In those days in Manchester, alcoholic contraband was the worst that Security had to worry about. Nowadays it's fifteen year old kids with semi-automatic handguns.

I usually get nervous around any kind of authority figure such as teachers or policemen or bouncers. And I always assume the security exits will start bleeping whenever I leave a shop, even though I'd never have the guts to do anything *remotely* illegal. As we neared the bouncers that night, I started to feel anxious and automatically began checking my pockets despite the fact I knew I'd done nothing wrong. I checked the inside of one pocket of my borrowed denim jacket and then reached across to the other. I felt something unusual and partially lifted it out.

"Kev – why the *fuck* is there a packet of potato cakes in your jacket?"

"Oh yeah. Must have forgotten to take them out."

For fuck's sake. Who the hell carries potato cakes in their jackets? I started to panic. I imagined the bouncers pissing themselves upon pulling those potato cakes from my jacket. Everyone in the queue would join in. I'd have preferred to have been discovered carrying drugs or weapons. At least then I may have earned some fearful respect from those in the queue if they'd thought I was a criminal drug lord rather than some savoury snack pervert. I was too near the front to quickly throw them anywhere. There was nothing I could do and so had to pray I'd avoid their roving hands. At that moment I was sweating more than Billy Heyes at Istanbul airport in *Midnight Express*. Thankfully, me and the potato cakes managed to bypass security. Although it turned out 'all-night' still wasn't long enough for me to cop off with a girl after all.

It would be such a buzz on the occasions when you *did* manage to get past the bouncers. I remember at Devilles you had to walk down a couple of steps and then wait in line to pay the entrance fee to the girl on the till. Once past her, you had to push this heavy black door and then it'd hit you all at once as you were met with the great sights and sounds that club had to offer. By sights, I obviously mean the girls in there and not the great décor and architectural splendour of the place. Like most nightclubs, it was a fucking dive, but I loved it all the same.

I met my second ever girlfriend in that club. Now, you've got to remember that I was only sixteen and I was still grateful for *any* female attention, whatever form it came in. I can't *actually* believe that I'm still feeling the need to apologise and make excuses for the appearance of ex-girlfriends almost twenty-two years later. *Like you fucking care anyway*. I know it *shouldn't* matter what people think as long as *I* found her attractive, but I've always needed that reassurance that other people would think my girlfriend was pretty too. Don't ask me why. It's pretty fucking pathetic when you think about it.

I remember one time in my early twenties when I'd taken this girl home that I'd met in some drunken haze in some horrible nightclub. I'd awoken the following morning and in the cold light of day, that girl wasn't looking quite as well as I'd remembered. I mean I'm sure she felt the same and it was *really* fucking awkward all round. Things got worse outside my flat as we were saying our goodbyes. We were both obviously complete novices at the one night stand game and were being awfully polite whilst trying to work out the correct protocol. The uneasy air was punctuated by a third party as I heard someone calling my name. I looked up to see one of my friends crossing the road and walking towards us.

Now I don't feel too good about this, but as my friend got close, I sort of stood in front of this girl in an attempt to obscure his view and disassociate myself from her. It was a pretty fucking lame attempt and it was blatantly obvious she was with me. I rambled on about something or other and then he finally walked on. I turned round to finish my goodbyes with that girl and I should have felt really bad, but all I could think about was how that bastard would be gleefully looking forward to telling everyone about how he'd seen me with some horror bag. I'm really *not* a nice person.

That second girlfriend that I was telling you about was quite tall but she was a bit bulky as well, if you know what I mean. She reminded me a bit of *Bernard*

161

Bresslaw – that guy out of the '*Carry On*' films. She didn't look like him – it was just the way she carried herself. Nobody in my group said anything derogatory about her but I got the feeling they weren't too impressed. If you really want to know, *I* wasn't too impressed. She did have really nice, long hair all the way down her back and I suppose she wasn't *that* bad looking all things considered. I mean she wasn't *repulsive* or anything. On reflection, that's probably not the best compliment you'd wanna receive off someone.

At that time in my life, I was totally in love with the idea of having a girlfriend and was happy to start seeing someone, even if I didn't necessarily find them *that* physically attractive. You're probably thinking I'm a right bastard talking about an ex-girlfriend this way, and I can't fucking argue with you to be honest. If it makes you feel any better, *she* dumped *me* in the end.

I can't even remember how I got talking to her in the first place, but you can bet it didn't involve any suave moves on my part. I told you how fucking hopeless I am at chatting girls up. It's a miracle I've ever had *any* girlfriends at all. I'd usually stare at someone I'd like the look of, but if they gave the slightest glance in return then I'd get totally embarrassed and not look at them again for a good twenty minutes. This would go on all night until they'd end up in the arms of some other bastard and I'd have the usual mixed emotions of regret, coupled with the relief that I then had an excuse not to have to approach them. I'll readily admit that it wasn't the best way to go about getting myself a girl.

On the odd occasion that I forced myself in front of someone, I'd usually just say 'hello' and then totally freeze. At that age, I desperately wanted to ask whether there was any chance I'd get to ejaculate anywhere remotely near them at some stage in the future. I realised though that I had to ask them about where they were from, what they did, and all manner of stuff I didn't want to know the answer to, before I could have the remotest chance of getting on to the good stuff. I probably sound like some kind of pervert to you but when a young guy chats someone up, it's all with the ejaculation stuff in mind. I appreciate it's not the most romantic notion in the world and I apologise from the bottom of my heart if I've shattered anyone's illusions.

She was a couple of years older than me and I guess I quite liked having someone a bit more mature to talk to. All in all, we got on reasonably well. She lived a couple of bus rides away but I still saw her fairly often although it was usually *me* who would make the long journey to see *her*. Even though I didn't fancy her that much, I still liked seeing her and being in her company. I already told you I liked the fact she was more grown up and obviously I was still young and horny and eager to get some action. Now I know you probably don't wanna know *anything* about this, but I managed to move on a stage in that time of sexual experimentation. I still didn't get to have sex, but we got our hands in each other pants so progress was made in my eyes.

It was pretty embarrassing stuff when I think back. The first time I got my hands in her pants, I remember we were in her bathroom and we'd been kissing and getting all steamed up. I'd unbuckled her jeans belt and managed to slide my hand into her knickers. I'd *like* to tell you that I was the consummate Casanova and that in seconds she was trembling in orgasmic delight. The reality was that I didn't have a fucking clue what I was doing. I just kept trying to push my finger inside her. I couldn't for the life of me understand why she'd keep pulling my hand so that my finger would come out and up slightly. I kept trying to push it back in and she'd keep pulling it out and lifting it up a bit. I remember getting a bit pissed off with it all, to be honest. Looking back, it probably wasn't *half* as pissed off as she would have been getting with the frustration of it all. Obviously now I understand where I was going wrong but back then clitoral stimulation was a pretty foreign concept to me. The finger fighting match was brought to an abrupt close when her young nephew attempted to open the bathroom door. He was met with screams and cries to '*Go away!*' whilst she hurriedly adjusted her clothing. I walked out past that little kid, feeling slightly guilty that a five year old boy had been battling the urge to urinate in his pants because I'd been fingering his aunty.

It was a few weeks later when she returned the 'favour'. I'd bunked off college and arranged to go and see her at her house, as the rest of her family were out. We ended up sat on the sofa and began chatting, with the TV on in the background. After a while, we were kissing passionately and I could feel her hand shifting slowly up my leg towards my groin. The moment I'd dreamt about was upon me! In one fell swoop, she'd undone my belt and flies and had reached in and grabbed me. It wasn't exactly the experience I'd hoped for. She'd pulled it free with her fingers and then leaned back whilst she stared down at it. It felt like she was examining me or something. I just sat there in silence with the cookery section of *This Morning* on in the background, whilst she poked and prodded me. She didn't exactly get a notepad out and start making annotations and sketching bar charts, but it wasn't far off. It was about as erotic as a trip to the doctors and my initial excitement had severely waned to the extent that my erection was rapidly losing patience. Richard Madeley wasn't helping matters and before I knew it, my penis looked like it was trying to retract inside my body. It isn't the most impressive of sights at its peak, but now it looked totally embarrassing as she continued to grasp onto it with her thumb and forefinger. After a few minutes more, and with the emotional detachment of a veteran angler throwing an unwanted fish back to sea, she let go without saying a word. I quickly tucked it back into my pants and fastened my belt. I don't know what the hell she was thinking and why she'd handled me like that, but it was pretty fucking embarrassing all the same. Still, the fact remained that I'd had a woman's hand on my cock and that was another thing I could tick off on my list of aspirational achievements.

Towards the end of summer, she left Manchester to go to University at the opposite end of the country. I was pretty gutted, but we'd said we'd keep things going despite the fact that she'd be fucking *miles* away. For the first fortnight, I wrote her a letter every day. Every *bleeding* day! I was a bit of a naïve romantic in those days and I obviously had way too much time on my hands. That level of devotion was promptly rewarded with a phone call advising me that our relationship was over. Despite our previous agreement, she now believed it was unlikely to work in view of the distance between us and had decided to call a halt to proceedings. She'd pretty much held the upper hand all the time I'd seen her and I suppose it wasn't really a surprise to me, deep down, that she wanted to end it. I recall numerous times during our relationship that she'd had the audacity to mention that she fancied black men and that she liked the idea of marrying a black or Asian guy and having mixed race kids. Not the most romantic of fucking topics! I guess I should have realised then that the writing was on the wall. I mean, I know people can change in relationships but there was fuck all this scrawny, white kid could have done to make that particular dream of hers come true.

I suppose breaking up with her was the best thing that could have happened in the circumstances, but it didn't feel like it at the time. It was also an early, valuable lesson in the fucked up rules of romance. It seemed that if you were *too* nice to someone, they'd probably end up taking you for granted and piss on you from a great height. It would take a while for me to acknowledge that fact properly though. It took a whole load more heartache in the form of my next girlfriend, Laura, but I'll tell you about her later.

A couple of months later, around Christmas time, I was out at this club with some friends and I bumped into the girl that had dumped me. By now I had met somebody else and was totally wrapped up in her. I'd found love and was of the opinion that everyone before her was irrelevant and didn't matter one iota. Regrettably, that chance encounter with my ex-girlfriend led to her practically stalking me for the next six months. Apparently she'd made a terrible mistake and hadn't realised what we had was so special. Regrettably for her, I'd subsequently realised that *I'd* made a terrible mistake in seeing her in the first place.

Fortunately she had to go back to University after the holidays, but it didn't stop me from being bombarded with phone calls and letters. I've got to admit that I got a bit of a perverse kick out of receiving those letters at first, being that *she'd* rejected me and being that I still remembered how much fucking money I'd wasted on stamps. It got to a stage though where the letters were becoming more and more frequent and the content became more and more bonkers. I even stopped opening them in the end when I recognised her writing on the envelope. She'd do things like cut passages about love out of the *Bible* and stick them on card and send them to me. By that stage, I felt a bit sorry for her. I guess rejection can make people go a bit fucking crazy at times.

Chapter Fifteen

It's winter right now and *really* cold outside. It's pretty fucking depressing at this time of year getting up for work in the mornings. I mean, it's pretty fucking depressing getting up for work at *any* time of the year, but it's even worse in the winter. It's always dark outside and it's tough leaving a warm bed to start getting ready. My house is *really* fucking cold in the mornings as well. I've got central heating but the cheap bastards who owned the house before me installed a dodgy cut-price boiler. I could put it on a timer so it'd come before I got up, but the thing is, it makes this awful fucking clanking noise that would wake me and the whole bleeding neighbourhood. I ought to get a new one but they're pretty damn costly and, besides, I always put things like that off.

I've got loads of stuff that needs doing around the house but give me half a chance and I'll put off doing any of it. I told you earlier that I'm hopeless at DIY and so I'm usually reliant on others to do that kind of thing for me. Getting a new boiler and arranging for all the other stuff to get done that needs doing would involve me having to ring people up and getting builders and the like in. I can't stand having people in my house that I *know*, so it's even more of a ball ache having total fucking strangers in. They always wanna make conversation instead of just getting on with things.

I bought that house 'cos it was opposite a park and I thought it would be great for my kids. It's also close to where my dad lives. I told you he's in his seventies now, so he'll probably need me to be close by to help out as he gets older. I haven't told him that though. He'd hate to admit for a second that he needed help of any sort. He's just like my gran, in that respect. To be perfectly honest, it's *him* that's been helping *me* out since I moved here. He knows I'm useless. I managed to fix the dishwasher once and, I swear, the shock nearly killed him. He said he was really proud of me. I know he was only trying to be nice but it was pretty condescending and made me realise just how hopeless he thinks I am. Anyway, I almost didn't buy that house and when I tell you why, you'll realise just what a soft bastard I actually am.

The thing is, a family was still living there when I went round for the first time to view it. They had two toddlers and a newborn to look after as well, so I figured it must have been a pretty tough time for them. It turned out they were renting and had been told they'd have to move out once it had been sold. I felt like a complete bastard as the mother showed me around the kid's bedrooms. I just wanted to get out of there as soon as possible. It seemed like I was intruding and it was apparent she had enough on her plate without having to answer my questions about the external brickwork. I went round that place in record time. I eventually bought the house but I felt incredibly guilty about that family and where they would be going. I didn't even fucking *know* them and they might have had everything planned and somewhere better to go, but it didn't stop me worrying. I worry a lot about things.

One of my earliest ever memories is walking past this field near where I used to live in that first house in Moss Side I told you about. There was this dog on the field and someone had tied some tin cans to its tail with a piece of string. Obviously it was a bit pissed off and was chasing its tail and going round in circles while trying to remove them. There was a group of older kids watching and laughing nearby. I know it wasn't *that* bad and I realise there are a hell of a lot of crueller things done to animals, but it didn't stop me feeling sick to the pit of my stomach. I was too young to go over and have a go at those kids, and I'm too cowardly to do something like that anyway. I walked away upset and kept thinking and worrying about that dog for the next few weeks. When you're that young you don't realise people can take pleasure from being cruel and it's a bit of a shock to experience.

I've *always* been a bit of a dick where animals are concerned. I get really stressed if ever I'm out and about and happen to see a stray dog or cat. I feel like I should be taking it home and looking after it. One time I was living in this flat in the centre of town and a skinny cat came running over, just as I was about to go in my front door. I started stroking it and it was circling my legs and mewing, like cats do. It kept on meowing really loudly and I guessed it must have been hungry but I had fuck all food in the house. I didn't even have any milk I could give it. I carried on stroking it for a few minutes and then quickly went inside the flat, deliberately avoiding eye contact as I closed the door behind me.

I remember sitting down in front of the television but I couldn't help but feel guilty about that cat. I kept switching channels whilst trying to convince myself the cat would be fine and that I should just forget about it and relax. I couldn't though. My brain wouldn't let me. I decided I had to go back outside and go and get that cat something to eat. I left the flat to see the cat still loitering near my door, sniffing about the plants. I walked back out into town, all the time cursing myself for being so pathetic.

Now, unfortunately, it happened to be late on a Sunday afternoon. As I was living in the centre of town there weren't any grocery stores open where I could go and buy cat food. The only thing open that sold food was McDonalds. It wasn't the ideal place to procure decent food for humans *or* animals. I was pretty fucking sure that cat didn't want a Happy Meal anyway. I went in the store and bought six chicken nuggets and walked the short journey back to my flat. Looking back, I'm not quite sure why I got chicken, when fish would have been the obvious meal for a cat. I guess when you're in the midst of a real emotional crisis then you just don't think straight. Anyhow, the furry fucker had looked starving and I was content that my small gesture would at least give it something to fill its belly.

As I got close to my front door, the cat came running over again and continued its high-pitched mewing. I went into the flat, got a small plate and started tearing the coating off the nuggets and ripping the bits of chicken up into little pieces. After a minute or two, I had a plate full of small, white chunks of reconstituted chicken meat. I walked back outside and placed the dish on the floor next to the cat. It sniffed the chicken for a few seconds and then turned and ran off without eating a single *fucking* morsel.

I swear I'm getting softer and worrying about things even more as I get older. For example, I reckon when people see bugs in their house then they'll usually step on them, or crush them with a tissue. I *have* to find a cup or plastic tub to catch and escort them out of the building unharmed. My twisted brain makes doubly sure I won't be tempted to execute any insects by attributing human names to the fuckers. So if there is the *slightest* contemplation in my mind about killing them, my brain will suddenly label that spider as 'Sidney', or that ant as 'Beryl', and it immediately feels a lot more fucking difficult to even consider ending their lives. Some of those insects are fast and I can spend about twenty bleeding minutes chasing round and trying to coax them into a cup so that I can let them go in the garden. I admit it – I'm nuts.

I can recall one time in particular when I was trying to get this ridiculously rapid spider into the safety of a plastic Tupperware container. The spider had really long, thin legs and kept darting away every time I got within a few centimetres. I was determined to catch it though, and let it loose in the garden. I spent fifteen minutes of thinking I'd captured it, only to find it'd raced away again. I was adamant that the next attempt would be successful. I edged ever so carefully to where it'd come to a stop near the skirting board. I hovered with bated breath as I held the container above my elusive prey. In one fell swoop I slammed the container down, incarcerating my arachnid friend. *Mission accomplished!*

Unfortunately my joy turned to dismay upon realising my swift action had brought the container down onto one of its legs. I slipped a sheet of paper under the container and flipped it over, before removing the sheet and examining the spider. Sure enough there was a detached limb stuck to the rim of the container and the spider was moving a bit more gingerly than prior to my ill-thought out action. Racked with guilt, I opened the back door and emptied that spider onto the garden path and into the night. I was consumed with angst – Brian wouldn't last a minute with his disability against some evil, predatory bird.

I'm over six feet tall and you'd think that height would give me the confidence to look after myself, but I'm a complete coward. Whenever any fights would break out near me at school or, in later years, at pub and clubs, then I'd run like the fucking wind as far away from any trouble as possible. If you've ever watched any nature programmes on TV, you'll be well aware that various species of animal have distinct biological facets to assist them in everyday life. Some have horns or claws for defence, or a particular colour of skin to help camouflage them from enemies. I reckon I inherited my long, spindly legs to help get me away from potential violence as soon as possible. I really hate fighting, or any kind of confrontation for that matter. To be honest, it makes me feel pretty sick.

When I was about fourteen, I used to play football on my own after school. There's this bank near to where my dad's shop is and it had a car park at the rear that was separated from the back of the barber shop by an alleyway. Anyway, the bank would shut around five o'clock, the staff would leave in their cars, and the car park would be closed. There were these big iron gates at two opposite ends of the car park. I'd usually wait until they'd been locked and all the staff had gone, before throwing my football over and scaling one of the gates. There were metal, mesh fences divided by concrete posts running all around the car park and they were great to use as football nets. I'd race about that car park pretending to be various footballers that played for Manchester City at that time.

My uncle used to take me to watch City from when I was about eight years old and I still go and watch them today. It was pretty good of him to do so. My mum and dad couldn't have afforded to get me tickets and he used to take me to every home game at Maine Road and quite a few away games too. It was a bit of a double-edged sword really, him taking me to games and initiating me into supporting City. I mean, it was great going to matches and having days out to other stadiums and all. When I first started going, I wasn't that interested in the actual game itself, but just used to stand mesmerised watching the people in the crowd. It was strange seeing adults getting so worked up and singing songs and veering from expletive-laden despair one minute to rapturous joy the next. That was all brilliant and I really looked forward to Saturday afternoons on the Kippax. But the fact of the matter was that the team I'd chosen to support weren't very good. At all.

City not being very good and failing to win anything other than the odd game wouldn't have been so bad in itself, but it was compounded by the fact that our big local rivals were Manchester United. They had all the glamorous star players and used to win trophy after trophy. Whenever we played them, my team didn't have a fucking prayer. I grew to hate United with almost as much of a passion as my love for City. I adored The Wedding Present's *George Best* LP but it would always be shifted to the back of my record collection so that filthy red strip wasn't on show.

The thing is City had been really great just before I was born, but my entry into the world coincided with their decline from league champions to perennial relegation strugglers. I couldn't help but feel the decline and the continuing malaise surrounding the club was partly down to *me* wanting them to win. I told you before, that it was survival of the fittest in the school playground, and supporting City just added to the ridicule that I already faced on a pretty regular fucking basis.

Back in that bank car park, I'd dribble at pace with the ball and leave imaginary defenders in my wake before slamming the ball into the corner of those wire mesh fences and wheeling away to celebrate in front of my non-existent adoring public. This one particular evening, I'd been running about like mad, smashing the ball left, right and centre against the fences. I was having a pretty good time. Then I noticed these two boys walking down the alleyway, approaching the car park.

I remember I stopped running about and quickly ceased all goal celebrations, as was often the case when anybody walked by. I just stared fixedly at the ball and started to do 'kick ups', whereby I'd attempt to knock the ball up in the air for as long as possible and not let it bounce on the ground. I pretended I was focused intently on keeping that ball in the air, but I felt pretty fucking uneasy as I heard the boys talking and then the clattering of the gate as they began to clamber over. I still didn't look up at them and I could hear them talking, but they were muttering quietly to each other so that I couldn't hear *exactly* what they were saying.

"Let us have a kick."

Any hope I had that they were gonna leave me alone disappeared in an instant. I knew that they didn't want a friendly game of football and that there was a pretty good chance I was in for a beautiful dose of violence. I was enclosed in that car park and the only way out was to scale one of those fences, and there was no fucking way I'd have been able to climb quickly enough without being caught.

I always look back on moments like that and fantasise about how it *could* have panned out. If only I'd have been like the tough characters in films I'd seen, and dealt with the situation differently. For example, Bruce Lee would probably have responded to their request with a wag of his finger and launched into one of those cunts with a flying kick, before despatching the other with a roundhouse. Henry Hill would have told them to go fuck themselves before banging their heads together and emptying the contents of a revolver into their flailing bodies. In the heat of the moment, I took neither of those options and plumped for the slightly less macho option of meekly passing them the ball whilst continuing to avoid eye contact.

They kicked the ball to each other, but it was obvious they were just toying with me whilst deciding my fate. I could tell from the way they kicked the ball that they were rubbish footballers and that made it even more apparent that they hadn't really come to have a game. They were in the mood for giving *me* a kicking instead. After a couple of minutes of booting the ball backwards and forwards, they lashed it across the car park and the taller of the two boys walked over to me. I remember looking up from the floor in time to see him raise his hands as he pushed me in the chest to send me staggering backwards a few steps. His accomplice suddenly spoke up.

"Hit him."

It probably would have been appropriate at that time to remind the loudmouthed twat of Derek Bentley's conviction and subsequent execution for his renowned 'Let him have it' quip prior to the murder of P.C. Sidney Miles in 1952. On reflection though, it probably wouldn't have deterred my assailants, and instead I took the only course of action available to your average coward – I started crying. They'd obviously not been expecting such a spineless reaction and just stood there nonplussed, instead of giving me the pummelling I was expecting. I turned away sobbing and began to climb the fence and make the short trip across the alleyway back to the shop. The two boys didn't try and stop me and were muttering something incomprehensible as I made my exit.

I remember I'd stopped crying by the time I'd walked back into the shop, but my dad could see the tear stains on my face and asked what was wrong. My lip began to quiver again as I told him what had happened. He didn't say a word and marched past me and I heard him leave the shop and make his way towards the alley. Minutes later, he returned but he wasn't alone. He'd bowled out into that alleyway and had frogmarched the two boys back into the shop. He barked at them to walk into the back room and then closed the door as he stormed in after them. I felt incredibly fucking embarrassed as I heard him verbally roasting those two fuckers. I also remember thinking '*What the hell is he doing*?' I mean, my father was holding two complete strangers against their will. *He'd fucking kidnapped two teenage boys*. It was definitely a criminal offence and was quite probably punishable by a prison sentence.

A few minutes later, the door opened and my dad escorted the two ashen-faced boys out of the shop. When they'd left, he turned around to face me and then spoke.

"Why didn't you just hit them back?"

He looked and sounded *incredibly* disappointed in me. I didn't know what to say. I already *knew* it was a fucking cowardly thing to just start crying. I already *knew* I should have hit them back. I already felt bad about those facts, but him saying that, and looking at me like I'd let him down, made me feel ten times worse. Fuck, I felt like crying again.

I'd like to think I'd deal with that situation differently now, but deep down I know I'd probably act in exactly the same way again. I'm just way too cowardly and emotional to deal with stuff. Although it's fucking ridiculous that I'm in tears when I watch something depressing on the news or watch a sad film, and yet I can't even cry at my own mother's funeral. I buried my head in the sand and didn't even address what was happening after I'd found half empty cans of lager hidden behind my mum's armchair. Yet I'd worry like crazy if I'd seen a dog on my way home that looked like a stray. The thing is I can't deal with stuff that I actually *really* fucking need to. And it's not like all that stuff disappears if I ignore it. It's *always* in the back of my mind.

Chapter Sixteen

About ten years ago, I was living in this small, rented flat in the centre of town. The flat where I'd seen that ungrateful cat. It was quite difficult to get on the waiting list for those flats, but my uncle had been offered one and had let me take it on instead. Turns out he'd found something else he preferred in a different area. It's not like those town flats were luxurious or grand or anything but they were in a great location above the main shopping centre in the middle of Manchester. I really enjoyed living there, it was pretty great. Anyway, one evening as I sat watching TV in that flat, the phone rang. When I picked up the receiver, I got a bit of a shock.

"Hiya Neil, it's Laura."

I would have been around twenty-eight at the time of that call and I'd not heard anything from her for at least seven years. She was my third girlfriend and I'd been *completely* besotted with her. I can't possibly exaggerate how head over heels in love I was. It might sound silly saying it now but even though I was just a sixteen year old boy, I was convinced I'd be with her for the rest of my life. I suppose I still love her now, even after all this time and everything she put me through.

I'd met her in that great club Devilles, which I told you about. It wasn't that long after the break up with my second girlfriend. I'd seen her in there before, but I never contemplated for one *second* that I'd stand a chance with her. She always appeared really confident and she used to get a lot of attention off other guys. I guess she was attractive in a pretty obvious way, if you know what I mean. She was quite small, and she had bright, shoulder-length blonde hair that framed a good-looking, tanned face, and a dazzling, white smile. She also had really large knockers, which I'm a big fan of.

I won't ever forget that first night when we ended up getting together. I'd noticed she'd glanced at me a few times when I'd walked past her in the club, and she'd held the look that fraction of a second longer, so that I knew it meant more than just a casual glance. Towards the end of the night, I remember accidentally on purpose ambling slowly down a corridor where I knew she was sat. She turned and looked at me as I walked by and flashed that beautiful smile. It was pretty obvious that she either liked me, or she was mentally ill. Either way it meant I stood a chance.

Unbelievably, I summoned up the courage to speak to her and uttered an opener like 'Hello', or something equally charming and witty. I can't exactly remember what we chatted about but we got on fantastically well that night and it seemed to be over in minutes. She was incredibly different to the all the other (two) girls I'd been with before. I fancied her immensely but she was quite down-to-earth and that made me feel dead relaxed being around her. At the end of the night, we had a kiss, which was *really* great. We exchanged phone numbers, although I was pretty fucking sure she'd wake up the following morning, realise her mistake, and kill herself.

I played it pretty cool after that and didn't ring her until the following afternoon. I actually wanted to ring the next morning but didn't want her to cotton onto the fact that I was a bit of a desperate loser. The call *would* have been earlier but it took me a hell of a long time to pluck up the courage and I slammed the receiver down many times partway through dialling. I remember that my heart was racing when I eventually dialled the whole number. The line connected and the ringing tone seemed to go on forever. I felt awfully panicky and just when I thought I'd be able to get away with postponing the call, a voice responded on the other end.

"Hello?"

It wasn't her.

"Hi. Is Laura there, please?"

"Who's calling?"

"Neil."

"Who?"

She'd obviously been going on about me all morning.

"NEIL."

"I'll just get her."

It was her mother that had answered the phone. It turns out that her parents were quite wealthy and lived in this really nice detached house in the south-west of Manchester. Her father was a self-made man who'd started out with nothing but eventually become a successful businessman. He was a great guy, all in all. I remember he was fairly short and had this really cheery disposition. He quite liked the sauce, if you know what I mean, and he always appeared pretty half cut whenever I'd go round. He seemed to just accept me at face value though and was always friendly.

One thing he *did* do, which was really fucking annoying, was grill me every time I went round to their house. Not about my intentions towards his daughter, or anything like that. What he'd start talking to me about were current news stories – political issues and the like. He'd ask my opinion on various world matters. I was still only sixteen and, to be honest, I didn't have a fucking clue what he was on about half the time. I was desperate to impress him though. I always knew I was gonna get those questions and so I'd end up watching the news and reading the papers prior to visiting their house. It's stressful enough going round and meeting your girlfriend's parents, without having to sit a fucking current affairs exam each and every time. Apart from that, he was a pretty good guy.

Her mother was always pleasant enough to me, but she made it pretty fucking obvious that she thought her daughter was *way* too good for me. To be honest, so did I. Her mother was one of those northern women you read about that transform into complete snobs after coming into money. Like I said, they'd both apparently had nothing at one stage, and it was *him* that had been successful enough for them to enjoy a better way of living. Despite her roots, she now thought she was a member of high society and she pretty much looked down her nose at me. I think she felt sorry for me in a way and assumed I was just a phase her daughter was going through.

I can't recall what was said on that first phone call with her but we still got on well, and arranged to meet at that club the following weekend. Saturday couldn't arrive soon enough for me and I remember that I bumped into her prior to going in. She was looking gorgeous again and I just couldn't believe my luck. For some unfathomable reason, she seemed to really like me too. We started seeing more and more of each other and I became absolutely smitten.

She was only seventeen but she'd already passed her driving test and her parents had bought her this gleaming white convertible *Volkswagen Beetle*, which had this retractable red canvas roof. She'd drive and pick me up pretty regularly and we'd go on days out or visit her friends. She got even more attention when she was driving about in that cool car. I remember one time, when she dropped me off one morning at this park where I used to play football. I played for a Sunday league team in North Manchester, near to where my dad lived. The team name was 'Racquets' which was a bit of a ridiculous fucking name for a football team but it was taken from the local sports shop that our manager owned. No other team dared take the piss though 'cos we had quite a few headcases in our squad. I had a couple of pals on the team but that morning when she dropped me off, *everybody* wanted to talk to me. I got a lot of respect off those teenage nutters for turning up in that car with a girl like Laura.

Although it was apparent that she liked me a lot, I

still always felt that she was too good for me and that I was really lucky to have her. The money thing didn't help matters either. She'd always have loads of cash due to her parents, whereas I never had a fucking bean. She had a big house and car and went on holiday about four times a year, and I had nothing. I even used to feel embarrassed about bringing her around to my house. That small terraced house just couldn't compare with her huge house and garden. I'm ashamed to admit it, but I was embarrassed about my mum too. She'd quite often be out of it and would be slurring her words, what with the drink or her medication or whatever, and it'd be pretty uncomfortable in front of Laura. Like I said before, I was largely oblivious to my mum's problems though and was too busy wrapped up in my own little world.

I always hated to admit to Laura that I couldn't afford to do things and I'd often just go along with whatever she wanted. I was totally infatuated with her and we were spending more and more time together. We used to be separated every few months when she'd go on some beach or skiing holiday, and it was unbearable being without her. She'd post me loads of letters though and would ring quite often too. The letters and calls made up for her absence and I'd be almost bursting with excitement on the days she'd return home and meet me.

She went skiing in France on a regular basis, something that I'd never done. It all seemed a glamorous world away from my experiences of egg butties in Abersoch. One time, I agreed to go with her to this dry ski slope that wasn't that far away from where we lived.

To be perfectly honest, I was fucking dreading it 'cos I knew I'd be awful. She had all her own expensive ski stuff and brought that along, whereas I had to hire some stuff from the place. As I'd never skied before, I had to go on the nursery slope with all the children and the physically infirm.

I'm really not built for activities like skiing or roller skating – my legs are way too long and I remember being nervous as hell approaching that small slope. I felt incredibly awkward and gangly and, as I put a ski forward onto the slope, I was convinced I was imminently destined to break several limbs. There was a thick rope down the middle of the course and I held firmly onto it as my skis made contact with that dry slope. It was definitely reminiscent of Bambi on ice as my legs seemed to go in completely different directions and I began to slide down the ice. My survival instinct kicked in and I remember desperately grasping at anything that went by, in a fraught attempt to retain my footing. I don't feel too great admitting it, but I was grabbing onto the duffle coats of children and dragging them over in an attempt to avoid falling to my doom. Seconds later, I was on my back sliding to the bottom with any remnant of pride long since fucking gone. I got those skis off as fast as I could and retreated to the sanctuary of the café. As I sipped a hard earned mug of hot chocolate, I watched Laura through the window as she masterfully commandeered the large slope that gave me shivers just by looking at it. Not for the first time in my life, I felt a bit of a dick.

I've got some great memories of being with Laura. One of the best times was at this bonfire night party at her house. I'd not been seeing her that long and she'd invited me to this family party in her garden on November the fifth. They were gonna build a big bonfire in the back garden and have fireworks and tonnes of food and drink. To be frank with you, I've never really liked bonfires and fireworks. I probably sound like a right miserable twat, but I really can't stand all the noise and I always worry about all the poor animals that spend the entire night scared stupid. I guess I've just never been in love with the idea of standing outside in the freezing cold watching a load of flashes and explosions. I've always loved sparklers though, like every other little girl.

I was really looking forward to being with Laura that night though, and I felt really great that she'd invited me to a family event. It probably sounds stupid but it made me feel a little more secure in the relationship. I've gotta tell you, it was a wonderful night. They'd got a pretty good bonfire going in the garden by the time I arrived and they had this old settee and armchairs lay out all around it. There was loads of food and drink and it felt really fantastic being part of the family. It was what I'd always imagined a normal family to be like. It was a million miles away from *my* home life. At one stage of the evening, when everybody was outside in the garden, me and Laura went inside the house and crept into the living room. We kept the lights off and kissed and cuddled for ages, until her mum started calling her name. It was just great and I was so happy. I *really* loved her.

It was even better later on in the evening. By that stage, everybody had gone inside the house and me and Laura ended up huddled together on that old sofa, in front of the bonfire. We didn't particularly say much but we were really close and it was lovely being alone and hugging her, while we watched the flames crackling away. I'd probably not felt that happy and content since that Sunday morning I told you about all those years before, when I'd just woken up and the church bells were ringing and my mum was hoovering and *Timi Yuro* was playing on the record player.

I lost my virginity to Laura and I was more than happy about it, I can tell you. We'd been invited around to one of her friend's houses and we were gonna stay the night and so I was pretty certain that I'd finally get to have sex. We'd kissed and messed about loads previously and that had all been great, but it was still a bit intimidating knowing we were finally going to sleep together. I knew she wasn't a virgin although I didn't really like to think about it, to be honest. It put a bit more pressure on me though, 'cos I was desperate that it would be ok. At the very least, I knew it couldn't be as bad as my skiing.

It was a wonderful night for sure and I don't think I would have liked to have done it for the first time in any other circumstances. We didn't get much sleep that night and I'm not exaggerating when I say we must have made love about seven or eight times across the course of that evening and morning. It wasn't quite the Don Juan style performance it sounds though, as each time probably lasted between 30 seconds and a minute. I loved every second of it though. It was a perfect night 'cos everything just seemed so right. I'd finally lost my virginity and it was to the girl I loved with all my heart. The girl that I could never, *ever* imagine being apart from. I guess I knew deep down though that something that made me feel *that* happy couldn't last.

We had loads of great times together and it's only those times that I wish I could remember. We managed to get away quite often thanks to her being able to drive and having that great car. I've got loads of fond memories of her speeding down the motorway to places like Blackpool while we both sung at the top of our lungs to tapes of James or The Wonder Stuff. I remember this other time when we were able to spend the whole weekend at Cardigan Bay in Wales. The country that I'd loathed whilst holidaying with my dad and step mum was transformed into somewhere idyllic with Laura. The entire time we were there was perfect, even the weather was fantastic. One of her friends came along too and we all got on really well. Her friends were always good with me despite the fact they all seemed to be quite wealthy and from totally different backgrounds to me. They all went to grammar schools and spoke without the Mancunian drawl that afflicted me. I couldn't help feeling inadequate around them. After one summer evening drinking at a pub, one of her friends offered to give me a lift home. I spent the entire journey stressing about what her pal would think when we pulled up outside my mum's tiny terraced house in the rough area of Manchester I lived. So much so, that I got her to drop me a good twenty minutes away to avoid any humiliation.

When I got home, my mum was wedged in her armchair, snoring away. Some nights it was almost impossible to wake her up as a result of the concoction of alcohol and pills she'd have consumed. I knew Laura's pal would more than likely be parking her car in the driveway of her large home before being greeted by well dressed, eloquent parents. It's difficult not to envy the secure family life enjoyed by others when you come from such a dysfunctional background. I couldn't for one minute imagine feeling comfortable enough to introduce my mum to Laura's parents. I already got the feeling that Laura pitied my mum. I knew for certain that any such meeting would result in her mother looking at me with even more disdain than ever before.

This sounds crazy but for a long time in my life whenever I thought about Laura, I'd recall this one time when she wasn't even there. It was a Saturday night, when she was away on holiday and I'd gone out to a club with some friends. Later that night, this girl started giving me the eye while we were dancing. Eventually she came across and tried it on with me. She was quite pretty and it was a nice confidence boost getting that attention, but I apologised and told her straight that I already had a girlfriend. I remember vividly standing on the dance floor in that club and thinking about Laura and feeling so happy. I knew for sure that I loved her deeply and I was certain that she felt the same. I thought that we'd never be apart and I couldn't contemplate being with anyone but her. Laura got loads of attention off other boys when we were out, but I knew she loved me. Perhaps it was just youthful naivety but it didn't cross my mind for one minute that she'd ever go with anybody else. It really didn't. When reality would finally hit home, I'd immediately recollect spurning the advances of that girl on that Saturday night, and my ill-judged sense of loyalty would ensure the feeling of humiliation was that much greater.

There were obvious signs after a year or so, that things weren't quite how they should have been. I guess I didn't want to accept them and so I ignored them and buried them in the back of my mind. One time, I got picked for the college football team and we had to play an away match at Manchester Grammar School in some cup competition. Manchester Grammar School was a privately funded all boy's school and was a world away from the shambolic institution that I attended. The fucked up education system that exists in this country ensured that all the kids from wealthy backgrounds at Manchester Grammar School would have a much better chance of succeeding in life than the poor bleeders who went to comprehensive schools like mine. We did pretty well against their team though and only lost by an odd goal in extra time. Laura was supposed to be picking me up after the match and all the other boys heads turned to stare at her as the Beetle roared into the car park at full time. I remember as I trundled off towards her with my kit bag in tow, that one of the grammar school boys turned to speak to me.

"Which one of your lot's with Laura?"

I told him it was me and he didn't respond other than to look me up and down. I didn't think to ask why he wanted to know, or even who he was. I just walked across to the car and jumped in before we sped off. It was only later on that I'd question myself as to how that boy knew her name. I was well aware she went to the all girl equivalent Grammar School but that still didn't explain how she was well known to half the fucking football team. It probably sounds to you now as though I'm overreacting about that incident but, in hindsight, it was one of a number of small warning signs I should have taken heed of. I made sure I was *totally* fucking oblivious to it all though.

The next indication I had that something was wrong was a hell of a lot more blatant. Not that I chose to accept it of course. We were at another family gathering of hers, only this time it was at her brother Nigel's house. He was an amiable enough guy and was always okay with me. He owned this sandwich shop near Sale in South Manchester and he ran it with his wife. I wasn't too keen on her though. She was big and loud and I always remember thinking that Laura's brother could have done a lot better than get together with her. The reason why I didn't like her wasn't anything to do with her appearance, but more her attitude. I don't know whether she was jealous of the way Laura looked, or the attention she got, or even whether she just didn't like Laura full stop, but she'd be fairly nasty and have a dig at her sister-in-law at every possible opportunity.

On this particular occasion, I remember we were all in the flat above their shop. Laura's mum and dad were there, along with her brother and his wife. Everyone was chatting away, albeit Nigel's wife was dictating the conversation as per usual. She'd been having a dig at Laura about something or other and then all of a sudden she said something which pretty much stunned everyone into a momentary silence.

"All I'm saying is that if Laura doesn't change her

ways then she's going to end up getting AIDS."

Whether her accusation had any substance or not, I think you'll agree it was a pretty fucking nasty thing to say. It was bad enough saying it to Laura and her family, but even worse saying it in front of me. I felt incredibly humiliated and didn't know where to look or what to say. She knew full well I was Laura's boyfriend but still went ahead and insinuated she was cheating on me without stopping for a second to consider how that would make me feel. Obviously everyone was really embarrassed and Laura's mother spoke up to tell that bitch to stop being silly, and the topic was quickly brushed aside. Afterwards, Laura made out her sister-in-law was just being spiteful and that she enjoyed saying horrible things about her. I sound really pathetic saying this, but I didn't make an issue out of it at all. I didn't wanna think about the connotations of what had been said. I told you that I really loved her, and I didn't want anything to spoil it. The reality of the situation was that her sister-in-law was probably doing me a favour by saying what she'd said. But at the time it just felt that she was trying to ruin everything. I tried really hard to forget what happened that day. I couldn't though.

I swear I never used to be the jealous type *at all*. Like I told you, I would never have dreamed she'd ever cheat on me. Even though I thought she was too good for me, I was convinced about how we felt about each other. The thought process of my teenage mind was quite simple. I believed she loved me and so therefore she must have been happy. And if she was happy, then why would she *want* to cheat, or do *anything* that could hurt me? The thing that her sister-in-law had said kept nagging in the back of my mind though. I needed something that would allay any fears I had once and for all.

I'd known for a while that Laura kept a diary in her bedroom and I knew any answers would be inside that diary. Part of me felt like I *had* to look and see what was written, but another part of me just didn't want to do it. For a start, I knew it wasn't morally right to look and read her private thoughts. Although I think the part of me that didn't want to look was driven by self-preservation and the thought that there was the distinct possibility that I might see something that would ultimately wreck our relationship.

I get that miserable nowadays with having to come to work every day that I occasionally buy lottery tickets. It's pretty fucking depressing when my only Plan B for life is winning the bleeding lottery. It's not like I think I've got a fucking hope in hell of winning either. But once I've bought a ticket then it makes life a little more bearable knowing that there is the *slightest* chance that I might win and not have to go to work anymore. The crazy thing though, is that a lot of the time I don't even check my ticket after the draw to see if I *have* won. I know that the chance of me winning is highly un-fucking-likely and I know that if I check my numbers, then I'll be disappointed. So by not checking my numbers I can still retain the hope that I might have won and that's enough to keep me going. It doesn't really make any sense but the rationale behind not checking those lottery numbers was the same rationale behind part of me not wanting to check her diary. I knew it'd only lead to heartache.

This one time, we were sat together in her bedroom when her dad called up to her for something or other. She ran down the stairs to go and speak to him leaving me all alone, just perched on the edge of her bed. Her diary wasn't hidden away and it was just *there*, enticingly sat upon her bedroom dresser. I really didn't want to do it but I had to for my own peace of mind. My heart was racing because I knew she could come running back up the stairs at any moment. To be honest, I think I *wanted* her to come back and stop me in my tracks. I felt ill as I reached across, grabbed the diary and opened it up.

She had written tonnes of entries inside that diary. She'd always written in a really distinctive way which reflected her personality. Her handwriting was easily recognisable 'cos the letters were always quite large and flowery. I mentioned to you that she used to write to me a lot, especially whenever she was on her frequent holidays abroad. Those letters were one of the things that I clung to whenever I was trying to dissuade myself about any possible infidelity. I reasoned with myself that the fact she had written those letters on her holiday proved her love for me. When we were apart, I would be constantly thinking about her, and those letters were evidence that she was constantly thinking about me. I loved receiving them and I'd read them over and over. I actually kept them for years in this old plastic carrier bag, along with those crazy letters from my second girlfriend and a host of old photographs. On the odd occasion, I'd get them out and read them all over again. I can't anymore though 'cos a jealous ex-girlfriend of mine threw them all out a few years ago.

It really upset me. I don't understand how anyone can get so resentful about somebody else's past.

Laura was a really intelligent girl. She always got top marks at her grammar school and she was incredibly eloquent. She was even fluent in French. Her letters were frequently romantic, and always interesting and comical. She was really quite funny and she'd often do a lot of these silly doodles in the letters. I remember one time she'd done this drawing on the back of the envelope. It was mostly covered up by the envelope flap so the postman wouldn't have known what it was. When I opened it there was this nude cartoon self portrait, complete with huge knockers and curly pubic hair. It was pretty childish but it made me smile a lot. I'd give anything to still have those letters.

I knew I didn't have much time to look through that diary 'cos she could have come back upstairs at any time. I hastily flicked through it, although I wasn't exactly sure what I was looking for. My heart continued to pound and my stomach hurt. I was desperately hoping I wouldn't discover anything of concern. I guess I knew that was a pretty fucking forlorn hope though and it didn't take long for my world to come crashing down. As I glanced through the pages, I came across a few entries mentioning other boys that she'd kissed and fumbled around with over recent months. The thing is I wasn't even shocked, 'cos deep down I think I already knew it. I really didn't wanna read any of the gory detail though and I quickly thumbed though the book until I got to the back cover.

As I neared the back of the diary, some scraps of paper fell out onto the floor. I reached down and picked them up off the carpet. There were about six pages of lined paper covered in blue ink. I started reading and a situation I thought couldn't get worse, suddenly got worse. It was a letter addressed to her off some guy from Denmark who she must have met on holiday. I skipped through the paragraphs but certain lines jumped out at me. I learned how much he liked *my* girlfriend and how much he missed *my* girlfriend. Then the tone shifted towards the end and it began to get pornographic. I remember that glued to one of the latter pages was this picture of a couple fucking that had been cut out of some hardcore porn magazine.

To cap it all off, the most disturbing part was at the end of that letter. He'd signed off and then underneath he'd done a sketch that filled most of the final page. It was a picture of a guy masturbating and ejaculating. I guess it was supposed to be him. It was quite a well detailed drawing although to be perfectly fucking honest, I really wasn't in the mood to appreciate its artistic merits. The most unpleasant bit of all was a message he'd written in the middle of the scrawled semen. The message said "This is for you, Laura." Obviously, the guy was a fucking *born* romantic.

I folded the letter up, put it back inside the diary, and returned it to the top of the dresser. I sat down on the edge of her bed. My head was banging and I felt physically sick. I had to put everything into some kind of context inside my head. It was pretty fucking obvious that the girl I loved more than anything in the world had been sleeping with half of Manchester and, when time permitted, half of Europe too. It may have helped that I already suspected something, but it was still pretty much worse than anything I could have imagined. I felt unbelievably humiliated. The only thing that kept flashing through my mind was that night that I told you about, where that girl had approached me and I'd turned her down. I kept thinking about how I'd rejected that girl while feeling incredibly happy about my girlfriend, when all the time she was most likely having sex with someone else. I thought about all of her friends that I'd met, about her mum and dad and her brother. Everyone must have known about it. Everyone apart from me. I felt really *fucking* stupid.

To tell you the truth, I couldn't make much sense of it. I mean, she'd always acted like she'd really loved me. She was always seeing me or ringing me. Even when she was out of the country, I told you she'd be sending me those great letters and ringing me. I just couldn't understand *why* she would do those things. Why did she need anybody else when we had each other and everything was so great?

I hid it all pretty well when she finally returned to the room. I just acted like normal, as if nothing had happened. I guess I should have gone ballistic and dumped her there and then. I should have ranted and raved and left her crying in a heap and walked away with some dignity. I know that's what you're all thinking. And I don't blame you. But if I'd have reacted in that way then I wouldn't have had Laura in my life anymore. That thought was worse than anything I'd just seen in that diary. If I'd have mentioned any of it to her, then I knew we'd have had to split up. And I really couldn't face that.

We'd been together over two years at that point

and it was the best two years of my short life. She was everything to me and life without her just wasn't an option. So I kept quiet. A while after, she went to study at Cambridge and therefore the times I got to see her became more and more infrequent. Being apart from her would have been tough enough before the diary incident. Now it would be a million times harder 'cos I knew she'd still be up to stuff, especially with her being away for such long periods. Like some kind of masochist, I still looked at her diary from time to time whenever the chance arose. Nothing had changed. I was still at her beck and call and she was still cheating.

One weekend, she invited me down to visit her in Cambridge for the first time. I got the train down to see her and she turned up to meet me at the station. Despite everything I'd discovered, I was still really looking forward to seeing her. As I'd always struggled to accept I was good enough for her, I guess I was able to excuse her actions on the basis I still believed I was lucky to have been chosen as her boyfriend. I know that sounds really pathetic. I think I was trying to bury it in the back of my mind and convince myself that it was just a phase she was going through and that everything could still work out as I'd originally envisaged.

She was smiling on the platform and she looked and acted genuinely happy to see me. I could never be angry at her when I saw her and I was mad at myself for it. It was awfully difficult because she didn't look like the girl that could be capable of those dreadful things described in her diary. She didn't look like the girl that could do something so cruel. She just looked like *my* Laura – the girl I'd fallen in love with and the girl I was supposed to be with forever. Regardless of my attempts to ignore reality, that trip to Cambridge would turn out to be the beginning of the end.

She spent much of the morning showing me around the city and the University where she studied and resided. While walking around the campus that afternoon, we bumped into these two guys she knew. She introduced me to them both and I was pretty fucking certain from his nervous, smirking reaction that she was carrying on with one of them. That moment was probably the ultimate fucking humiliation and made me finally realise that something had to be said.

Later that evening, when we were back in her small flat, I managed to find the courage to force myself to broach the subject. I told her that I knew she'd been seeing other people and that I'd seen it all in her diary. I desperately wanted her to tell me it had all been some horrible mistake; that she loved me more than anything and that everything would change and be okay. She didn't though. Instead she became incredibly angry and defensive and said that she thought I was disgusting for looking in her diary. *As if I'd betrayed her! You couldn't fucking make it up!* I got *really* upset and *really* angry. I grabbed this little alarm clock that she had and I launched it against the wall in a rage. It was total frustration on my part. By her not denying anything, it somehow made all the stuff I'd read in that diary become real. I sat down in a chair and cried and cried. I couldn't kid myself any longer and I was extremely upset and angry that she'd ruined what we had. But most of all I was frustrated and angry with myself. I knew that despite everything she had done, I still couldn't leave her and I hated myself for it.

I eventually calmed down and we ended up hugging and lying down on her bed. That led to us having sex before we finally drifted off to sleep in each other's arms. I had to catch a train in the early hours of the following day and so there was no further conversation between us. I'd left college at that stage and found employment in a temporary office job at the Department of Health and Social Security in the centre of Manchester. I needed to get there on time and therefore rushed off about half past four in the morning. I quickly got dressed and kissed her forehead and told her I loved her before closing the door behind me and racing through the halls and the short distance to the train station.

It took a few months before I came to my senses and realised that things couldn't carry on the way they had been. I *still* couldn't be without her but I told myself that I was a fool, and if *she* was going to act that way, then so should I. It didn't make any sense whatsoever but I started seeing other girls and I guess it probably helped give me a little bit of self-esteem back. The fucked up thing was when I started cheating on her and acting *less* interested, then she suddenly started to act a lot better towards me. It was like she had finally realised that she was in danger of losing me. From that moment on she was all over me and *she* was the one getting upset all the time. Seeing other people had given me the confidence to move on though, and our relationship had no chance of being repaired.

All that emotional heartache with Laura really fucked me up for a very long time. I'd cheat on a lot of other girlfriends from that moment on. It was pretty fucking indefensible, although my messed up reasoning got me through it. I believed that being betrayed by some girl wouldn't hurt as bad if I cheated on them first. It all boiled down to the humiliation I felt when thinking back to that night in that club when I'd done the honourable thing and turned that girl down for the misguided notion that I was in a mutually loving relationship. It's no fucking excuse though and I cheated on some really decent girls who didn't deserve that kind of behaviour in a million years. I'll always feel a bastard about it and I'll always regret it.

I hardly ever spoke to Laura following our split. I rang her from a phone box outside the hospital after my mum died though. I don't know why. She was the only person I wanted to call at that particular moment. She thought I was joking, for some bizarre fucking reason. To tell you the truth, she couldn't wait to get off the phone. I think she had someone there or something. I really needed her to be nice to me at that moment, but she was obviously preoccupied. I don't exactly know how I expected her to respond but I guess I thought it might make me feel better, hearing her voice. As it turns out she was pretty cold. When I put the receiver down and stood there alone in that phone box, I felt even worse than before.

It's weird but whenever I've broken up with anyone, I always just look back and dwell on the good times we shared. And when I think of those good times, then I start wishing I was back together with them. For example, with Laura, I always think about that bonfire night and that night at her friend's house and I think of her fondly 'cos I try and black out all of the horrible stuff. Since my mum died, *all* I ever seem to think about is the bad stuff. For example, certain occasions when I wasn't that nice to her, or when I should have acted better or been more appreciative towards her. I just never automatically think about the nice times I spent with her and I'm constantly feeling guilty. I swear my brain fucking hates me.

You can imagine how it was such a shock to receive that phone call from Laura all those years later, in that flat in the centre of town. Apparently, she had gotten the phone number off my dad after telling him that she needed to speak to me. It was extraordinarily strange hearing her voice after all that time. I can't really put into words how it felt hearing that warm and familiar voice again. Feelings of love and disillusion all suddenly resurfaced. It was apparent from her tone that something was wrong. She explained to me that she was in a bad state and had felt compelled to contact me. It turned out that she had come home from work early one evening and had caught her boyfriend in the midst of having sex with another woman. She said it had devastated her and it had made her realise how I must have felt all those years earlier. Therefore she'd felt the need to ring me and apologise for what she'd put me through.

I regret it now but I didn't show her the slightest bit of sympathy. I told her it had fucked up all my future relationships and that what she had done had hurt me more than she would ever know. She was quite upset on the other end of the line and it really didn't make me feel better getting any of that stuff off my chest.

I had every right to be bitter and angry towards her because any memories of the special relationship we had will always be tarnished by what she did.

The fact of the matter is, I wasn't even angry anymore.

I was just sad.

Chapter Seventeen

When I did start work at the Department of Health and Social Security, it was always with the intention of it being on a temporary basis. I still didn't have a fucking clue what I wanted to do for a living but I thought I'd stay there for a year just to experience what work was like. It was pretty much as dull as I thought it would be. Following on from that stint in the civil service, I planned to go to university and hoped during that time I'd become enlightened as to what my career path should be.

Working in that office would probably have been a lot worse than it actually was, if it hadn't been for the fact that I was always fully aware that I was only there temporarily. At that young age, I was lucky enough to be able to do what I wanted. Some of those poor fuckers in that office had been there for years and destined to stay in that job forever unless they were fortunate enough to end up succumbing to a fatal heart attack or some other early demise. When you get to the stage in life where you have long term financial responsibilities, like a mortgage and a family, then they have you by the balls and the freedom of choice you have as a youngster completely disappears. It's a bit rich me telling you this though. Despite experiencing what office life was like and despite knowing how vapid and unfulfilling working in an office is, I still ended up spending most of my life in one. It wasn't a career choice at all, but I started work in one after university with the notion that I'd do it until I decided what I really wanted to do with my life. Seventeen bleeding years later, I'm still sat in an office waiting for some inspiration.

There's this song you might have heard by Morrissey from one of his earlier albums. The song tells the tale of this girl who's got a lift home off some guy and how she spends the whole journey lamenting how pitiful her life has ended up. She bemoans and questions how she's ended up living the very life she'd always planned on avoiding. It's pretty fucking great and the lyrics are really apt, as far as I'm concerned. That particular song resonates with me a lot. He's a great lyricist is Morrissey. His writing is incredibly clever and witty. I don't like admitting to having heroes in my life, but he is definitely one of them. I told you my mum got to be a big admirer of him too, despite his lyrics and melodies being a world away from her main idol, Cliff Richard.

The year spent in that office at the Department of Health and Social Security passed pretty quickly, to be honest. I remember the office itself was really long and filled with row upon row of desks that were usually occupied by mountains of files, telephones and members of staff all equally as bored witless as me. I, and the other people on that office floor, had the job of assessing claims from people who believed that they qualified for a government disability allowance. It was my responsibility to process their claims in my sexy role as an 'Administrative Assistant'. We'd start by sending some guy out to assess a claimant and that guy would report back to us as to whether he believed they'd qualified for the financial allowance. So our job would basically entail us ringing up some poor one-legged bleeder and telling them they were entitled to fuck all and to stop bothering us. *Pretty fucking nice, eh?*

There were a few decent enough people in that office. I didn't care for most of them, but some were pretty good guys. The boss was a bit of a sourpuss but fortunately enough he remained in his office for the most part and we rarely saw him. I can remember he was this miserable looking short guy with wiry, grey hair, big glasses and largely non-descript features. He was even more boring than he looked. Even though I was only there a year, there was one time when I managed to get into trouble off the boss. I'm usually relatively quiet and dull, so it really wasn't like me to get into any bother.

I told you that office was really long and I remember thinking one day that it would make a great football pitch. I knew I had to stay late one Friday and I'd brought in this little foam football with the intention of killing some time with it. Occasionally you'd have to take turns working late to provide cover for the phones. That particular Friday evening, most people had gone home with only the skeleton staff remaining. By the end of the working week, everyone was eager to leave that place and return home and so there was seldom anybody there past five-thirty who didn't have to be. I got the ball out and kicked it across to this other young kid who'd also drawn the short straw of a Friday late. We launched that ball up and down the office. It was good fun. We started getting a little rowdy though and we'd end up chasing down the office to try and get the ball off each other. At one stage, we kicked the ball down the far side of the office and ran like mad to be the first to win it. As we closed in on the target, we both slid to the floor with our legs ending up in a tangle as we fought for possession. All of a sudden, we were rudely interrupted.

"What the hell is going on? Both of you, in my office, first thing Monday morning!"

Fuck. The boss was still around after all. He had us bang to rights though. We couldn't really explain away how we'd come to be sprawled on the floor, fighting over a miniature foam football, when we should have been sat at our desks filling in forms.

On the Monday morning, he wanted to know why I'd brought a foam football into work in the first place. I told him I'd bought it at lunch for my dog, which I thought was a pretty good response considering I had to think on my feet. I didn't even *have* a fucking dog but I was confident he wouldn't follow up on my story. We both got bollocked though, which was only to be expected. There were no more foam football antics during the rest of my time at the Department of Health and Social Security but I'm in no doubt the entire civil service breathed a sigh of relief at the exit of this particular renegade bad boy.

Right the way through my year at that office, I was still living with my mum in a house in South Manchester. I didn't earn much money in that job and I made sure as little as possible went back to her. Although it meant I had a bit of cash to spend for the first time in my life, it also meant I had something else to reflect on and feel guilty about after she died. I mentioned to you earlier that we often had to move house whenever my uncle wanted to sell the one we were in and move us to another place he owned. It was a bit crazy and they were never the most glamorous of places, but it was still good of him to let us stay in those houses. Throughout that year I worked, before I left to go to university, my mum was okay most of the time. After a few weeks of her being fine, I always remember thinking that her depression must have been cured. It was usually wishful thinking on my part though 'cos just as things would seem to be okay, she'd have to be admitted back into hospital.

I got pretty mad with her about it sometimes but, like I've said, it was just brought about through frustration. I only wanted things to be 'normal'. I couldn't understand what the hell depression was and I still don't. I told you earlier that all the doctors ever seemed to do was keep prescribing her different concoctions of pills. Some days she'd be really out of it and I didn't know how to handle it at all. I wouldn't go and see her when she was in hospital and I relied on my uncle to tell me when she'd be coming back home. I felt down when I thought about it so I just ignored the situation.

I've never been one to get sick really but I had to go to hospital myself around that time. It's pretty fucking embarrassing explaining what was wrong with me, but seeing as I've spilled my guts on everything else that's happened in my life, I may as well tell you about this. I know you're probably thinking you don't even *wanna* know what it was, but I'll tell you nonetheless.

211

It's nothing *too* gruesome, but like I said, it was an embarrassing condition to suffer with. Now, I'm no doctor or anything, but I'll explain it as best I can.

You know there's a tube that carries urine from your bladder to the outside? Well apparently that tube is called the urethra and the doctors told me that there was some scar tissue inside, possibly caused by kidney stones. Over time this was causing the urethra to narrow which resulted in less room for fluid to escape. I'd notice that whenever I went for a pee I'd sometimes take fucking *forever* to finish. It was always embarrassing going in public toilets when three or four guys would come and go before I'd finished at the urinal. I hate using public toilets at the best of times and so it was a nightmare having to be in there even longer than usual. I've always loathed standing there at those urinals, especially at work where you're more likely to know the person stood next to you.

The main reason I always feel uncomfortable peeing in those situations is that sometimes you'll get guys start chatting to you, while you're stood there just trying to take a leak. Small talk in any situation is bad enough, but it's even worse when some stranger starts chatting as you're both stood next to each other with your dicks out, urinating away. Occasionally if there's already somebody stood at a urinal when I walk in, then I sometimes just *can't* go. As I'm stood there, not peeing, I start to think that the other guy will be wondering why I'm not peeing, and assume I'm some kind of pervert who's just walked in to check out penises. My mind is really fucking crazy.

That condition I was suffering with started to get

gradually worse over time. Occasionally, I wouldn't be able to wee at all and the pain was pretty fucking immense, I can tell you. Obviously, I faced it like every other problem I faced in my life and that's by ignoring it and hoping that it'd go away. It didn't though and it just got more acute.

I've always disliked having to go to the doctors or the hospital; sitting around in a packed waiting room and being forced to listen to a god-awful instrumental version of 'Everything I Do (I Do It For You)' on repeat, with coughing and spluttering strangers wedged into chairs either side of you. The experience is ghastly enough when you're suffering with flu or dislocated limbs, but you've got to believe me when I tell you, its worsened tenfold if you know you've gotta go and talk about your faulty knob.

This one time, the pain had gotten unbearable and I had to face the unenviable task of heading to hospital with the knowledge that loads of doctors and nurses would be poking and examining my privates. Believe you me, with genitals like mine, you *really* don't want them on general exhibition.

When I got to the hospital, the doctor eventually explained that the only course of action was to insert a tube into my bladder in order to empty it. This didn't seem too frightening until I began to realise *how* they were gonna get that fucking tube into my bladder. And because I'd left it so late and I was in absolute agony, they had to try and get the tube in as quickly as possible. Now I'm quite a private kind of guy that likes to keep himself to himself. Lying half naked from the waist down on a hospital trolley in the middle of a busy ward as a doctor and three student nurses try to push a rubber tube up my penis, *wasn't* the most comfortable of situations for me to be in. Although, to be honest the pain had gotten that bad by that stage that I couldn't have cared less if they'd have been trying to get that tube in my half naked body on the centre circle in front of eighty thousand people at Wembley stadium – I just wanted to wee.

Prior to setting off for the hospital, I'd been suffering in excruciating agony at home. I'd felt really feverish and had been bent double, whilst slowly pacing about the bathroom. I was desperate to alleviate the intense pain and had even resulted to constantly murmuring 'Please God, let me wee.' It probably wasn't the regular kind of assistance He was used to being asked for. I don't even believe in God, but desperate times et cetera, et cetera.

I'd not even questioned the existence of God at that age, and it probably wasn't until I was in my twenties that I began to think how ridiculous a concept it actually was. Nowadays, I find it absolutely incredulous, and quite fucking distressing, how many seemingly intelligent people claim to believe in a God and live their lives according to the philosophy of organised religion. It seems pretty fucking apparent to me that organised religion has evolved from general ignorance of the mysteries of life, and has just been reaffirmed over the ages through brainwashing and indoctrination at an early age.

I say it's distressing 'cos no matter how harmless certain religious beliefs seem, they usually incorporate some level of oppression and discrimination whether it be the subjugation of women; Catholicism refusing to sanction the use of contraception to end the suffering and deaths of millions; or the downright hatred of homosexuality by seemingly every bleeding religious organisation there is. And then there's the absurdity of faith schools. Why not let kids grow up and decide about things for themselves rather than try to force them to support a particular team? In my eyes, faith schools are promoting social division and alienation before children have even had a *chance* to integrate. It's barmy.

A friend of mine once tried to justify the existence of the Catholic Church to me by praising the fact that they provide comfort to bereaved individuals and promote a moralistic way of life. Now, it's all well and good that religion provides comfort to those suffering bereavement, with tales of some kind of heaven or paradise in the afterlife, but the fact of the matter is that *nobody* has a bleeding clue what happens to you when you die. Somebody telling you that your dead gran is partying in some utopian paradise might be what you *want* to hear, but it doesn't give it any more credibility than tooth fairies, Father Christmas or hob fucking goblins. It does, however, prevent any potential suicide bomber from wavering from their murderous act, safe in the knowledge that they're straight off to bed virgins in paradise as soon as they've pressed the detonator. As for the moralistic line that is peddled by religion, it's full of fucking contradictions. You really shouldn't need advice from a man in a dress as to what is right and wrong anyway. I reckon good parenting and a dose of common sense should be alright by anyone.

Don't get me wrong though. I'd absolutely love it if there is a God up there, and some kind of afterlife. The thought of dropping dead and that being *that*, is pretty fucking depressing and it's no wonder people are so eager to take in the stuff spouted in churches, mosques and synagogues. The way I see it though, is that if there is some kind of loving God up there, then I'd hope He wouldn't hold it against me, or anybody else for that matter, that had harboured any doubts about His existence.

I can't see why just because somebody wore a turban or a skullcap throughout their life (and *at least* one of those forms of headgear is being needlessly worn by millions of people), or regularly attended a church or a mosque on a regular basis, that they would get preference in the bestowing of the key to an afterlife. I can't for the life of me understand why people would spend *any* of the precious time we have on Earth praying and saying thanks to some form of spiritual being. I mean, in my opinion, God must be a bit of an egotistical bleeder if He expects every fucker to spend their entire lives praising Him. If He existed, I'd like to think that He'd think a lot more of people if they spent less time creeping and sucking up, and more time doing something worthwhile, like helping the needy, or something. It really makes no fucking sense to me at all.

You gotta hand it to those religious guys though; they definitely know how to handle P.R. You'd think that when disasters occur or horrible crimes are committed, that people would begin to question the existence of something that could create such horror.

They've always got a bleeding answer though. Usually, it's something like 'God is testing your faith', although I, for one, could think of better ways to test people's faith than causing a tsunami; or giving somebody's young child a lethal fucking dose of leukaemia. And when there *is* a disaster, like a plane crash or something, and hundreds of people die, it's the same fucking cop out. Instead of people saying 'That God is a bit of a twat, allowing that plane to crash and killing all those people', you hear things like 'There were two survivors – it's a miracle!' I swear – that guy can't lose. I wish people treated me like that in everyday life. I got lambasted at school for a poor performance in a maths test 'cos they concentrated on the seventy-three per cent I didn't get, rather than the thirty-seven per cent I did.

Anyway, God didn't intervene with my urethra and I had to rely on boring old science again. I was told afterwards that the pain from that condition has been described as the nearest a man can get to experiencing the trauma of child birth. Obviously, I felt fucking *honoured* to have been able to have that experience. It was also explained to me that it was an incredibly uncommon condition to be experienced by someone of my age and was usually likely to be found in elderly men. *Aren't I one lucky fucker*! Following the procedure, I had to stay in the hospital for a few days with a catheter attached. This marvellous contraption comprises a tube inserted into the penis to divert any urine into a plastic bag, and the bag is then attached to a metal frame. It was *quite* the fashion accessory.

I had to stay on a hospital ward with a load of other poor bastards who'd also had problems with their waterworks. I was the youngest on the ward *by far*, with the majority of the other beds filled by men that had long since reached pensionable age. I'm a really light sleeper and I remember struggling to get much shut eye whilst staying on that ward. Whenever I did get off to sleep, I kept having nightmares about zombies and, looking back, it was probably due to the fact that my bed was next to the toilet and so those old fuckers were constantly shuffling slowly past me throughout the night. I ended up having to endure a cystoscopy, where they surgically scraped away the blockage before they allowed me to leave hospital.

The misery didn't end when I left that hospital, 'cos I had to keep that catheter attached for a week or so before I could return and finally have it removed. Whilst at home, the tube was attached to a smaller plastic bag which had to be tied to my leg and drained in the toilet as and when it became full. I *did* tell you it was a fucking embarrassing condition.

Before I'd had to go into hospital, I'd been seeing this girl for a few weeks. She had long blonde frizzy hair and an abundance of moles. The one thing I remember about her was that she was part of a local amateur swimming club and used to swim competitively against other clubs across the country. She used to get a buzz from showing me how great her stomach muscles were. I swear her stomach was rock hard from all that swimming. Anyway, when I'd returned home from hospital, she rang me and said that she wanted to come round and see me. I told her that I'd been in hospital but I just said that it was due to an operation on my stomach. I really didn't like explaining the old 'plastic tube in my penis' tale to anyone, so I gave her that vague explanation about a stomach procedure. I told her I didn't feel up to seeing anyone, and I really didn't. I felt pretty fucking weak still, and sex, for probably the first and possibly only time in my life, was the last thing on my mind. She was pretty insistent though and so I eventually relented on the basis that she'd said she would just call for five minutes and then go home.

She came round later that evening, about nine o'clock, and my mum had already gone to bed. She went to bed early quite often and I put it down to the medication she was on, although it might well have been my conversation. I heard a knock at the door and I shuffled across the hall and let her in. I knew I looked ill, and I felt pretty fucking rough, but straight away she said I looked poorly and that made me feel even worse.

We sat down on the sofa and exchanged pleasantries and all that sort of thing that I told you I hate to do. Unfortunately, it was pretty fucking apparent from an early stage that she was in a bit of a horny mood. She'd obviously been feeling a bit frisky and had come round for some action, on the pretence that she was concerned about my well being. In any normal circumstances, I'd have had her knickers off before the kettle boiled, but I really wasn't in any state to take advantage of the situation. She was totally oblivious to the fact, but I was obviously aware that her roaming hands might uncover one *hell* of a passion killer.

At nineteen years of age, I wasn't that worldly-wise, but I was pretty fucking certain that in a list of the most effective aphrodisiacs of all time, a warm bag of piss attached to your inner thigh probably wouldn't have made the top ten. The next twenty minutes were a re-enactment of Kenneth Williams' character in *Carry on Nurse* when he gets chased around the room by an amorous Hattie Jacques. When I used to watch those films, I used to think that it was pretty fucking ludicrous that any possible situation could arise whereby a man would run scared from the lusty attentions of a woman. It didn't cross my mind that it might be because they had a bag of urine about their being.

The operation cleared the condition and for a few months the sheer velocity of my pee could have put out wildfires. It didn't last though and the condition returned a few years later, and I had to go through the whole fucking process again. I've not had it return since though (touch wood) and hopefully that was the last bleeding time.

Chapter Eighteen

When I went away to university in Bristol, the thing that I struggled with most was having to make decisions and be responsible for myself. Like I said before, the only reason I went away in the first place was because I thought it was expected of me, and also because I didn't know what else I wanted to do. I guess it also kind of appealed because I'd then be far away from home. Considering the issues with my mum, it would be a case of 'out of sight, out of mind.'

Up until going away, I'd pretty much had my hand held throughout my life with regard to decision making. Whether it be through my parents making judgements for me, or by teachers telling me I had to have work completed by certain times. At university, it was a shock to be suddenly treated as an adult. I had to pay bills, make my own meals and motivate myself to attend lectures and to study. It's pretty fucking stressful and you suddenly realise how much easier life is when you're a kid and you've nothing of importance to worry about.

There are so many simple pleasures in life too, when you're young. I remember that I used to really love it in the winter months when it got darker earlier and bitterly cold out. Weirdly, unlike most kids, I didn't particularly like it when it snowed so much, 'cos there'd always be some bastard that'd pack a snowball real tight until it was just ice, and then launch it at your head.

What I always loved was when it was really cold in the mornings – just cold enough to leave a white frost across the grass and just cold enough to turn all the puddles to ice. I always remember getting great enjoyment out of finding puddles that had iced over and then digging my heel into the ice or stepping on frozen puddles and seeing the ice crack underfoot. I'm still tempted to do it when I see iced over puddles now, but it's not the done thing when you're an adult and, besides, it would be spoiling it for some kid who'd be looking for untouched ice puddles like I used to do.

I didn't do too great during university. I just wasn't interested in either the subject matter of my courses or the majority of the people that I had to converse with on a daily basis. The lecture rooms and the bars at that university would either be filled with people I didn't know, or people that I *wished* I didn't know. Don't get me wrong, I did meet some nice people there – I mean I met and went out with this amazing girl who I still love to this day – but, as pathetic as it sounds, I felt pretty fucking homesick the entire time I was there.

I ended up travelling back home almost every other weekend and it cost me a fucking fortune that I honestly didn't have. I couldn't afford to get the train home and so more often than not, I'd have to get the coach back. It took about four bleeding hours, which was a real ball ache, although it felt worthwhile when that coach finally turned into the centre of Manchester. I'd stare through the window and see all the familiar roads and buildings of my city. To be honest, I was sick of the place before I left for Bristol, but it felt really emotional coming back for the first time. I told you I was way too soft about stuff. As that coach pulled into Chorlton Street coach station, I realised how much I missed Manchester. I mean, most of it was still a right fucking dump, but I'd missed it. It's pretty hard to explain why.

I'd use football as the main rationale for why I needed to return home every other weekend. I didn't miss many City home matches despite living down in Bristol for three years. It was only partially the reason I wanted to go back, but people wouldn't have understood about me being homesick. And I didn't want to get into the guilt about being away from my mum. Not that I ended up seeing her that much while I was there, but it eased my conscience just being in the same city. I told you I couldn't afford the travelling, and I couldn't really afford the football either. I was entitled to grant funding for the first year or so and then the Government decided to introduce student loans, which meant I would be saddled with debt from an early age. I obviously felt really fucking lucky to be one of the first generation of students to move from grant funding to a lifetime of debt.

The money I received from those grants and loans didn't go far and I got into quite a bit of trouble, financially. I was pretty immature about things and I used to just withdraw cash and ignore the bank statements which dropped onto my doormat. This resulted in me receiving an absolute mountain of overdraft charges and fees. Some of the other students got money off their parents but there was no fucking way that was gonna be a realistic option for me. I didn't even know if my dad could have afforded to give me any money but I knew he wouldn't be too forthcoming with it anyway. And then there was my mum. She used to ring and ask *me* for money!

Whenever she rang, I knew it was because she'd be having money problems. So rather than being happy to hear from her, my heart would sink when I'd answer the phone and listen to her voice on the other end of the line. I really couldn't afford to give her any money but it didn't make me feel any less guilty about it. When I came off the phone, I'd be worrying about her needing that money and I'd be scared she'd be getting herself into a state again. I thought it would make things easier being so far away from home, but it just made it worse.

During the first year of university, I lived in this decrepit house in a ridiculously rough area of Bristol. The house was freezing and crawling with ugly cockroaches and even uglier students. The electricity always used to run out and the kitchen was far too filthy for any of us to ever contemplate making anything edible. I'd not exactly lived the life of luxury back in Manchester but that mangy house took the biscuit. There wasn't even a telephone and so I ended up having to use a nearby phone box. Whenever I'd have to make a call, there'd usually be pimps, drug dealers and gruesome looking prostitutes lining the pavement opposite the phone box. Unbeknownst to those welcoming locals, their unsightly smiles and flashes of cleavage were wasted on me as I couldn't afford drugs *or* prostitutes. I was barely able to scrape together enough for the takeaway pizza that would become my staple diet at university.

I used to survive off those margherita pizzas and was even reduced to Dairylea triangles, Ritz crackers and crisps when the money situation became increasingly dire. In all honesty, I don't think my diet's changed that much for the better since way back then.

Living in that dump was especially difficult to swallow knowing that I shouldn't have been there in the first place. I should have been entitled to an automatic place in the university halls of residence, being that I'd come to Bristol from a fair distance away. Unfortunately the university fucked up my application and by the time it was sorted, all the places in those halls of residence had been taken. Things improved after the first year 'cos I got a house with that girl I'd started seeing, along with a few mutual friends. A friend of that girl even managed to fix me up with a job, through her father, at a bank in Manchester during the summer holidays. To be quite frank, it was a fucking godsend 'cos I *really* needed the money.

One of the biggest dilemmas I had to face whilst being away at university wasn't to do with my courses, accommodation or my lack of culinary skills. It was to do with my hair. Whenever I was in need of a haircut throughout my childhood and teenage years, I'd hang around my dad's shop and he'd see to me once the last customer of the day had left, the sign in the window had been flipped over to 'CLOSED', the blinds had been drawn and the front door locked. As you can imagine, he was less than enthused at having to carry on cutting hair at the end of his working day and his apathetic approach was usually reflected in the quality of the final haircut I received. Although I never helped matters by constantly barking orders throughout the haircut instead of just letting him get on with it. The worst thing of all for him though, was that he wouldn't even get paid.

My hair grows quite quickly – it always has done. When I was away at university, there came a time when I knew I couldn't leave it until the next time I was home and at my dad's shop. When you're nineteen and you've never visited a hairdressing salon before it can be quite intimidating. I knew, for example, that you had to make appointments in lots of places – you couldn't just walk in off the street. Then there was the issue of what to ask for. As I said, I usually yapped instructions at my dad throughout the entire haircut.

"Just cut it a bit shorter there … and a bit more there … and can you take that up just slightly … that's enough … no, actually cut it a bit shorter just there".

I was a real pain. I knew I wouldn't be able to say all that to a hairdresser that wasn't my dad. I began to worry about the terminology and just exactly what it was I was supposed to request. *And should I tip them?* I knew some places expected you to tip and some didn't. There was so much to worry about I almost didn't bother, but one look in the mirror and I realised I didn't have much choice.

During that first year away, I decided to walk around my new home in that rough area of Bristol in the hope of finding a suitable barber shop. I was pleased to discover one in a row of shops not five minutes from my front door. I remember tentatively walking past a couple of times to peer in and weigh it up. I was immediately relieved to see there were no customers inside as I'd fearfully imagined a packed shop of people guffawing in unison as they watched me struggle to get to grips with the terminology and conventions that were the norm when visiting the hairdressers. At long last, I plucked up the courage and pushed open the heavy shop door. A young black woman popped her head out from the door nearest the till.

"Er … do I have to make an appointment?"

She looked quizzically at me.

"No."

She gestured at me to sit down in a spacious chair in front of a mirror. I followed her instruction and she enveloped me in a purple gown. She wasn't too bleeding friendly and it *really* didn't help my nerves.

"Ok. What do you want doing?"

This was it. The big question. I had to think quickly.

"Er … can you just cut it a bit shorter?"

I remember spending the next couple of minutes mulling over the idiocy of my request. *Can you just cut it a bit shorter?* Well, *obviously* she was going to cut it and that would invariably mean it would be shorter. She must have thought I was a total idiot.

As she ran a comb through my hair and I began to hear the snipping of the scissors, I started to relax and idly look around and take in my surroundings. I gazed into the large mirror in front of me and the reflection of the empty seats and row of large hair dryers. The walls were adorned with photographs of male and female models sporting differing hairstyles. It was at that moment I realised why my hairdresser had looked slightly perplexed upon my arrival.

"Move your head forward please."

I dug my chin into my chest and heard the electric clippers whir into life and felt the cold, sharp metal against the nape of my neck. Seconds later, I felt a scratch and the clippers went silent as they were switched off.

"Oh no I'm sorry. The blade was a bit too sharp and its cut your neck a little bit. Sorry about that."

She reached down and put her fingers into some kind of white cream and smeared it onto my neck in an attempt to stem the bleeding. In typically English fashion, I didn't complain and instead thanked her and told her the haircut was fine. I paid and hot-footed it out of the shop with half a haircut and a wounded neck.

Whilst walking the short journey back to my Bristolian utopia, my mind drifted back to those photographs of the models on the walls. All the models had been black. They'd all been sporting thick, wiry afro hairstyles. No wonder she had looked at me strangely when I walked in! No wonder those clippers caused me an injury when they weren't used to cutting thin, straight hair! My first trip to a hairdressers outside of the family and I end up getting my fucking head hacked off at an Afro-Caribbean hair salon. I really am an absolute dick.

I told you I loved going back home at the weekends and it was great to see my friends, as well as being able to go to the football. We'd still go out on Saturday nights, although things had taken a turn for the worse at the clubs I used to enjoy going to so much. When I first started going out, there was a general division in the type of bars and clubs you could go to. There would be places that usually played guitar based 'indie' type music that would attract me and my friends and would predominantly be frequented by students. The antithesis existed in the form of bars and clubs that played generic pop and dance music comprising stuff that was in the charts at the time and usually heard on daytime *Radio One*. From my experience, these clubs were largely attended by local testosterone-fuelled knuckleheads and their female equivalents.

Around two a.m., the clubs would all close and we'd often have to negotiate a path home past those rough bars and clubs. Regrettably this meant we would regularly bump into swathes of bone-headed bastards heading home after their night out at 'Rotters'. Many of these revellers would be itching to finish off the night by beating up individuals that looked any different to themselves. As is the general law of being a student, I had lots of hair. I had fashioned it into a bob haircut and this, maybe quite rightly, made me a target for the hateful throng. Fortunately it was usually just verbal abuse that came my way.

"You fuckin' puff!"

This was quite a regular taunt from drunken fuckwits. There were numerous occasions when I was eager to point out that I had a girl on my arm, and that the fact they were *without* female company might lead one to conclude that it was *they* who were the likelier advocates of homosexual activity. I would always refrain though, for fear of receiving a good fucking beating. My good friend Simon had his hair styled into an awesome quiff and luckily their attention would usually be switched to him, allowing me to make my cowardly escape.

During one summer holiday break back in Manchester, we all decided to return to that great club Devilles we used to go to. The one that I told you about earlier. None of us had been there for some time and we were all looking forward to the night out. We knew it wasn't going to be *exactly* the same as years previous, as the music scene had changed, and with it the bars and clubs had changed too. Indie music had become very popular and had slowly begun to populate the music charts, and with this crossover of music into the mainstream came the crossover of those knuckleheads into the bars and clubs I'd previously had such fond memories of. Dance music, especially 'House' music, had also become extremely well-liked and bars and clubs were eager to exploit its popularity.

That evening, we started as usual with a few drinks beforehand in a couple of bars around town. It was good to see everyone again after being away and the atmosphere was really great. After leaving those bars, we walked towards that club, still upbeat and in high spirits. It was strange making that journey after all that time and lots of memories came rushing back as we walked down the steps, paid the entrance fee, and opened the door to the main club area.

Inside it was almost unrecognisable as the club that we'd loved so much during our adolescent years. It wasn't so much the layout of the place, which remained exactly the same and still comprised two separate areas, each with its own DJ booth and dance floor. And those two areas were still separated by corridors on each side which ran parallel to each other. The familiarity ended there. The room at the farthest side was the busiest, although it appeared to be packed with uncouth looking teenagers. A strong odour of Vicks Vapour Rub hung heavy in the air. The DJ in that room was playing tuneless dance music and various males had relieved themselves of their upper garments as they danced in a trance-like state. Many had whistles tied around their necks and these were occasionally blown to further pollute our ears. We were fucking strangers in our own home.

We quickly retreated into the other room where the music was slightly more palatable, albeit not in the same league as what we were used to hearing in Devilles. That side of the club was practically empty, but we decided to get a drink, sit down and make the most of it. At one point, it seemed like there was going to be a rare glimpse of sunshine amidst the gloom. Our ears pricked up as the oscillating guitar intro of The Smiths 'How Soon Is Now?' filled the air and we all left our seats and made our way onto the dance floor. As I was rapidly becoming accustomed to in my life, all joy was short-lived and despair quickly set in as the anticipated vocals of Morrissey failed to materialise and we were left swaying to 'Hippy Chick' by eighties one-hit wonders Soho. I was more than ready to leave.

I spent the majority of my university years not doing much studying during term time and working at the bank during the holidays. I remember one term when the phone rang one night, at a house I was sharing with my girlfriend and a few other students. One of my friends answered and then passed me the receiver. It was my step mum. She was the *last* fucking person I'd expected to ring because, thankfully, she'd not tried to contact me since I'd left to move in with my mum.

"Neil? It's Blanche. I'm just ringing to let you know your mum tried to commit suicide last night."

I had to ask her to repeat herself because it didn't register the first time.

"Your mum tried to kill herself."

I didn't quite understand the point of her ringing me and telling me that news, being that I was so far away from home and my mum. And she could have *at the very least* sweetened that fucking pill instead of being so blunt about it.

She went on to say that my mum was ok and was currently in hospital. She also added that it wasn't the first time that my mum had tried to take her own life. I didn't say much in response, as far as I can recall. It was a bit of a shock and I wasn't sure *how* to respond. I just wanted her to shut up and go away. I wanted to put the phone down and run off. She ended the call by explaining that she had wanted to let me know and would ring again if she had any more news. She didn't even bother asking if I was ok or anything. I really didn't want that news and if I *had* to receive it, I would have liked it to have been from my dad.

I put the phone down, not really sure what to do next. I obviously felt quite upset and I started to feel panicky at being so far away from home. I didn't want to face anybody there in the room and I walked out of the door and onto the landing. I'd been in an okay mood prior to the telephone ringing but was now irate that she'd rang with that information. I couldn't think straight. I was angry at her and I was angry at my mum for doing something so stupid. I was also angry at myself for being so far away. At that moment, all I *should* have been thinking about was my mum's welfare. Instead, I kept reflecting upon the fact she'd been content to end her life, despite knowing she wouldn't ever see me and my sister again. I couldn't rationalise why my mum could think that way. I remember I felt incredibly sorry for myself and tears began rolling down my face. I wanted to scream in anger and frustration, but I was trying to stifle any noise. I didn't want anyone hearing any commotion 'cos it would just lead to loads of questions.

I remained on the landing at the top of a flight of stairs facing cheap, stained glass windows that looked out onto the back garden. You could tell it was really thin, inexpensive glass in those window frames. The landlord hadn't spent much money on anything in that house and you could feel the cold air permeating the glass. I couldn't even begin to tell you why, but I clenched my right hand into a fist and I punched right through one of the small panes of glass. I looked down at my hand and there was a small cut, which I hadn't expected. The others came out of the living room onto the landing, saw the broken window and wanted to know what was wrong. I felt sick, and their questions and their attention, along with the blood on my hand, just made me cry even harder.

I've heard it said that people who take their own lives are 'brave' and 'courageous' and I readily admit that it must take some guts to kill yourself. It's a desperate fucking act but, in my eyes, it's also a selfish, cowardly act too. My mum might have felt depressed enough to believe she'd be better off not living, but it's not a particularly fucking nice thing to do to your surviving friends and family. It's difficult enough coming to terms with the death of a loved one, but I can well imagine that grief is multiplied in the event of a suicide. If you lose someone and you know it could have been avoided then there can often be a lot of anger during the grieving process. When the only person that anger can be directed at is the person you're grieving for then it must result in some pretty desperate mixed emotions. I understand depression is a disease though and I guess it can make people do irrational things – I only wish I could have helped somehow.

Looking back to those times at university, I was a bit of an emotional wreck. I probably *seemed* okay on the outside to everyone else, but my head was one hell of a mess. I remember towards the end of my third year when one of my lecturers called me into his office. My course work had been piss poor across the year and so I knew I wasn't being summoned for any positive reasons. I sat down and he explained that he wanted to know why I was usually absent for his Friday afternoon lectures. Because the coach journey home took all of fucking eternity, I usually had to catch it around Friday lunchtime in order to get home for the weekend. I admit I barely made *any* of those psychology classes.

I started out by advising him that I needed to get

home on Fridays but then for some reason that I can't explain, I started to tell him about my mum and what had been happening. I got all worked up and started bawling my bleeding eyes out again. He was a bit taken aback and asked whether the university could do anything. He said that it must be affecting my work, and did I want him to get it taken into consideration when my dissertation was being marked. I should have said yes, and then I might have got a half decent grade out of it. But I declined 'cos I didn't want to blame my mum for how fucking poor that dissertation was. I don't even know why I told him all that stuff about her 'cos I had barely said a word to anyone else, but it just seemed easier saying all those things to someone who was pretty much a stranger.

I could tell he didn't wanna fucking hear it, that's for sure.

Chapter Nineteen

I told you I'm in my late thirties now and I know, relatively speaking, it's still quite young, but it doesn't *feel* fucking young, I can tell you. I remember back when I was in my late-teens, that thirty years of age sounded incredibly old. My mind and body feel incredibly ancient some days but I suppose I don't look too bad for my age. *For my age*. Those three fucking words are a killer. Not so long back I'd sometimes get compliments about how I looked and I still do on the odd occasion, but nowadays it'll be 'You look good, *for your age*.' It kind of ruins the whole bleeding compliment tagging those three little words on the end.

I've managed to fight them off for a while, but I've noticed more and more grey hairs coming through lately. I know you don't notice yourself physically ageing 'cos you don't notice the gradual effect in the mirror every day, but those grey fuckers are a sure sign I'm no spring fucking chicken anymore. I wonder how someone like Brigitte Bardot feels when she looks in the mirror these days? I was watching one of her DVDs the other night; it was a compilation of all these crazy French pop videos from the sixties. Seeing how beautiful she was on that DVD, and knowing how she is now, made me feel even more depressed about growing old and the whole ageing process. At least I'll never be able to picture my mum as some decrepit, elderly pensioner.

Whenever I think of her, I try and remember her as she was in that photo I told you about.

It's probably 'cos my mum passed quite young and I know it's totally crazy, but a couple of times recently I've had these stomach pains in the middle of the night and I've managed to convince myself that I was gonna die like her. I know it's unlikely but I still can't help having that nagging worry in my mind, especially considering how she was fine one minute and then gone forever the next.

I'm forever having stupid fucking thoughts about all kinds of stuff. For example, I'll tell you about this crazy thing that I do sometimes. If I'm walking somewhere late at night and it's all quiet, I start imagining some actor doing the same walk as me for some *Crimewatch* reconstruction on the television. It's a pretty mad thing to do, and pretty bleeding egotistical to think my murder would make that *Crimewatch* programme anyway. I suppose it's a more glamorous way to go than just dying in hospital of bowel problems like my mum did. Knowing my luck though, if I *did* get murdered and if I *did* get on *Crimewatch*, they'd probably have my step mum on as the family representative. She'd appeal for information and nobody would ring up because everyone would hate her. And I bet she'd probably wear that same horrible, fucking dark blue suit she wore when she married my dad.

It's not just my appearance changing that I hate; I really don't like change full stop. Manchester has transformed a lot since I returned home from being at university. The town centre was pretty fucking grim back then and it took the I.R.A. bombing the place in

1996 before any kind of modernisation occurred. The whole town centre looks pretty fucking swanky now, and a world away from how it was prior to that terrorist attack, but I still miss the way it used to be. At the time they were there, I never thought for one single second that I'd ever miss the horrible fucking yellow tiles that used to decorate the outside of the Arndale Centre, but perversely enough I do.

It doesn't make any sense, but even though I resent a lot of my past, and even though a lot of things have changed for the better, I still get nostalgic and yearn for things to be the way they were. For example, I don't like the fact I can't go into John Menzies or Woolworths anymore. I don't like not being able to stand up at football matches and enjoy the atmosphere that brings. I don't like the fact that Opal Fruits became Starburst and that Marathon bars became Snickers. And I also hate the fact that I live in a country where the fucking inhabitants require Simon Cowell to tell them what music to listen to and Richard & *fucking* Judy to tell them what books to read.

I really enjoy living in the midst of a busy city and so obviously it was great having a flat right in the city centre. I know some people prefer the countryside, and I do like to visit those places, but I'd always choose living in the hustle and bustle of a city over the tranquillity of a rural village. Some days I'd enjoy spending hours browsing in record shops or book shops. Other days, when the weather was ok, I'd relax in the middle of town listening to my Sony Sports Walkman while watching the people walk by. The one downside to living in town was the number of people who'd constantly try to interrupt you from going about your daily business. There are people who want petitions signing, people who are trying to offload leaflets, people trying to get you to sign up to some charity or other – some days walking down the main city street is like trying to navigate a slalom course as you attempt to avoid the fuckers.

I remember this one afternoon when I'd just left my flat and was heading out to pick up some groceries. I'd barely ventured onto the street when this guy thrust a leaflet into my hand. I'm too polite to ever refuse and I grabbed it and thrust it into my jeans pocket without giving it a single glance. I assumed it was a flyer advertising some trendy nightclub and I felt quite good that the guy had thought I looked the type they'd want in that trendy club. You'd get quite a lot of people handing out leaflets for various nightclubs and, to be honest, I didn't get offered those leaflets very much anymore at my age. As I walked into Tesco, I had an extra bounce in my step about the fact that I obviously still had a youthful look about me.

Later on, after I'd got home and put the shopping away, I switched the TV on and sat down to relax. I'd forgotten all about that leaflet but at some stage during the evening I reached into my pocket and pulled out the crumpled pamphlet. I remember opening it up and staring at it in disbelief. I *had* expected to see perhaps a picture of some scantily-clad, foxy-looking girls in excessive make-up dancing away. I thought there'd be some blurb about a trendy new club and its great drinks promotions and shite music. Instead, I sat staring at a crude drawing of a grotty, cluttered room with a man sat on the edge of a bed with his head in his hands. The drawing was accompanied by a block of text in bold, inky black letters.

'Lonely?'

'Depressed?'

'Suicidal?'

'Why not come and join our prayer meeting on Sunday afternoon at......'

I was pretty fucking sure those foxy-looking girls and drinks promotions wouldn't be at that prayer meeting. I couldn't *believe* that guy must have thought I looked an ideal candidate for one of those leaflets. I'd been in good spirits earlier that day as I made my way to the shops. Now, thanks to that leaflet, I *did* feel fucking depressed.

I can recall that I.R.A. attack pretty well 'cos at the time that they'd decided to bomb the city centre of Manchester, I just happened to be living in my small, rented flat in the city centre of Manchester. *What a stroke of fucking luck that was.* I obviously recall the Saturday morning that it happened quite clearly. I wasn't going to mention this first bit, but fuck it, I might as well. You see, I'd been seeing some girl at the time, but had gone out with pals the Friday night before the bombing and ended up returning home with a girl that *wasn't* my girlfriend. I know – I'm a right bastard.

Anyway, the following morning we were both woken by the sound of someone hammering on the front door. I wasn't expecting anybody and automatically panicked at the thought that it might be my girlfriend. My natural cowardly instincts kicked in as I feared a beating on the back of my infidelity. Fortunately, I'd already told the girl in my bed about the girlfriend situation and so it made the romantic request to quickly dress and exit through the downstairs window, a little fucking easier. I waited a couple of minutes and composed myself before opening the front door, only to find there wasn't a soul around. I managed to convince myself that it must have been kids messing about and went back inside my flat. I momentarily considered chasing after the girl that had leapt through my window to reassure her that her life wasn't in danger after all, but quickly dismissed the thought. I proceeded to place two rounds of bread into the toaster, switch on the TV and relax on my bed.

A minute or so later, I remember hearing the sound of the freshly toasted bread resurfacing and strolling back towards the kitchen. Before retrieving the butter from the fridge, I had another quick look outside to see if there were any kids knocking about. As I peered outside, one of the neighbours strolled past and advised me that everybody had to leave their flats because of a bomb scare. Apparently we were all to make our way to a police cordon at the bottom of the flats. So, the knocking on the door had been a helpful warning about a bomb and not an irate girlfriend after all. Strangely enough though, the bomb seemed less of a threat.

Whenever security alarms are going off, or I hear things about fire and bomb warnings, I'd usually just presume it was a test or a hoax. Up until that point in my life, they'd always *been* false alarms. On that basis, I accepted this particular instruction with a sigh and dawdled whilst getting ready. Being I'm a huge coward, if I'd thought for *one second* that it *was* a real bomb then the likelihood is I'd have broken the land speed record to reach that police cordon. I remember I looked about my flat for something to wear and saw my crumpled suit, from the previous day, strewn across the floor. I resigned myself to the probability that I'd be back in my flat in ten minutes or so and, with it being the nearest thing to hand, I put the suit back on. I locked up and made my way across the car park to the main shopping thoroughfare.

It was quite an eerie sight that greeted me when I exited that car park. Normally at that time on a Saturday morning, the place would have been teeming with shoppers, but there wasn't a soul to be seen, save for a policeman standing on the corner. About four hundred yards away, I remember I could see the police cordon at the end of an adjacent street and there was a mass of people hoarded behind it. A policeman was gesturing me over and I sauntered across and took my place with all the others.

I must have been stood there for about ten minutes in that crumpled suit, wishing I'd brought my toast with me, and wondering how long it was gonna be before they'd remove the cordon and let everyone go about their business. All of a sudden, there was an almighty bang, and glass started showering down from the huge old buildings that lined the street we were all stood in. It's strange but your natural reaction to a loud explosion like that is just to start running like the wind. Everybody ran away from the cordon before coming to a stop a few hundred yards down the street and questioning what the fuck they were running for. People were stood around bewildered as to what had just happened. It's a strange sensation being on the receiving end of an attack and nowhere to direct your anger.

Even though everyone had been aware that there had been a bomb threat, it was still a big fucking shock to hear that booming noise and see the destruction the explosive had caused. Nobody around me seemed to be injured and it was difficult to assess exactly where the bomb blast had originated from. I wanted to go and check that my flat and all my belongings were okay but the aftermath of the blast resulted in the police pushing everybody further and further away from the city centre.

I spent the whole fucking day stood in that creased suit on the edge of town, not knowing when I'd be able to return home. It was mid-July and probably the only day in the entire fucking year that Manchester was bathed in hot sunshine. I was stood at the front of the ever retreating cordon, sweating in my trousers, shirt and jacket whilst everybody around me was dressed in shorts and t-shirts. The police didn't have a bleeding clue and couldn't even give me an estimate as to when people would be able to return. I was advised to go home and I had to explain about a hundred fucking times that my home *was* in town and I wasn't just hanging around in the hope that Dorothy *fucking* Perkins was gonna re-open.

I ended up having to sleep at my dad's house that night and it would be about three weeks before I could return to my flat to get some belongings, and about three months before I got to return there to live. I literally only had that crumpled suit that I'd left the house in and I had little choice in the first few days other than to wear some of my dad's clothes. My dad has never been much of a trendsetter and for those few days I half expected the Fashion Police to come knocking and throw the book at me for my half mast brown slacks and floral mustard shirt.

I was allowed to stay in another flat on the opposite side of town for the short term although it was difficult getting comfortable when I wasn't sure how long I was gonna be there. The authorities were unsure whether the structure of the building which housed my flat was safe and it had been mooted that the whole building might have to be demolished. As you can imagine that was a fucking *great* piece of news to receive.

They allowed us to return to our flats after about three weeks, accompanied by a fireman. We were to grab as many important belongings as we could carry in one trip, on the premise we might never be allowed to go back again. We were only supposed to get clothes and other essentials, but there was no fucking way I was gonna leave any expensive stuff in that flat. Especially when I knew that I might never get to see any of it again.

Unfortunately, the only thing I possessed that was worth remotely *anything* was this really heavy desktop computer and the accompanying monitor, which also weighed a ton. The lift to the flats wasn't safe and so we had to climb five flights of stairs to get to my front door. The fireman who escorted me waited outside the door and told me to go in and pack a box for us each to carry. I filled one box with clothes and bits of other stuff and put it to one side. I looked across at my computer and decided there was no fucking way I was leaving it to be demolished. I lowered it into the largest box, alongside the monitor, and then scattered some clothes over the top. I gave it a practice lift and swiftly decided I'd take the other box instead. I lifted up the box with clothes in and called the fireman in to grab the other one. I acted like my box was heavy, but it was pretty light, to tell you the truth. He, on the other hand, nearly gave himself a fucking hernia as he struggled to get that computer-laden box down five flights of stairs. *God bless our emergency services*.

Like I told you, it was about three fucking months before I was able to move back into my flat. To be quite honest, I was just relieved that it didn't have to be demolished. It comes to something though, when I'm feeling pretty lucky 'cos my home hasn't had to be bleeding bulldozed. When bad things happens to you, like becoming homeless after a bomb, or your body deciding it doesn't wanna wee anymore, then you start to feel like you're not exactly the luckiest bastard in the world.

I told you I hate change, but a change in fucking fortune at that stage of my life wouldn't have gone amiss.

Chapter Twenty

When I'd returned to Manchester from university, my mum had moved into a small flat in the south of the city. It wasn't large enough for me to be able to share it with her and that's why I moved into that flat in town. The only other option would have been to move back with my dad and step mum, but I *really* didn't want to entertain that particular option. I went back to work at that bank, as I still hadn't decided what job I wanted to do. The money came in handy, although I was far from being well-off. My salary was pretty fucking paltry.

I used to go and see my mum quite a bit when I'd moved back to Manchester. Actually, I don't know why I'm saying that – I probably didn't go and see her *anywhere* near as much as a son should see his mother. I guess I'm trying to make myself sound a nicer person than I am, although it's probably a bit too late in the story for that. When I did see her, it would usually be at my sister's house 'cos my mum used to go there a lot and keep my sister company and help out with her kids. My mum's health seemed to be in a decent state and I knew she hadn't been back to Prestwich Hospital for some time. Obviously I didn't broach the subject with her, and I was aware she was still on a lot of medication, but generally she seemed to be in better spirits for the most part. It was fucking ironic then, after having battled so long with mental issues and having overcome the subsequent related suicide attempts, that it would be something so seemingly fucking *insignificant* that would kill her.

As far as I remember, my mum had begun complaining of stomach pains. No-one thought that much of it initially but then they'd gotten that bad that she had to get an ambulance to hospital, late one night. Apparently, she was examined and was sent back home after being diagnosed with nothing more serious than constipation. The next thing we heard was that she was being rushed back into hospital after somebody had re-examined her x–ray and noticed a tear in her bowel.

I remember going over to see her at St. Mary's Hospital in South Manchester. It was about a ten minute bus ride from that flat she'd been living in. I wasn't looking forward to going to that hospital but at least I knew the other patients would be 'normal' people. It would make a change from the nut house where we'd usually had to go and visit her. As is the norm with hospital visits, it took a bleeding lifetime to track down the ward that she was staying in. My sister had come along with me and when we finally reached the bed my mum was in, she was out for the count. She didn't look ill or anything. It just looked like she was sleeping.

After a short time, one of the nurses came across to us and told us that one of the doctors wanted to have a chat with us privately. That should have rang some big fucking alarm bells, but it really didn't. It hadn't crossed our minds that our mum was suffering with something serious, let alone life-threatening. We got shepherded into this pokey little office and this doctor sat us down and started speaking. He was quite a young guy and he was obviously trying to look as solemn as he possibly could. He started off by apologising and saying that he had some bad news for us. He told us that she had a tear in her bowel, and that it was a serious condition. I can't remember how he phrased it exactly but he said this stuff had been leaking out of that tear and was poisoning her, and this had caused her body to shut down. Then he apologised again and said that he didn't think that she'd make it.

My sister was incredibly upset and started bawling really loudly. I didn't cry and I didn't even feel sad, because it just seemed unbelievably fucking surreal. I mean, she was fine a day or so ago. She'd only had a stomach ache. There wasn't *really* anything wrong with her. *She couldn't just die – not like that.* I *honestly* didn't believe what he was saying and I was certain inside that he was mistaken, and therefore I didn't feel the slightest bit sad.

We got escorted out of the office and one of the nurses was trying her best to calm my sister down. I just wanted her to shut up, to be honest, 'cos people were looking at us and I always feel really uncomfortable when the attention is on me. It took her some time to calm down, but she eventually did. Afterwards we went and sat back with my mum for a while. Neither of us said anything and so we just sat in silence until my sister had to leave. She needed to go home for her kids and so I was left sat all alone with my mum. She was still sleeping soundly. Even though I knew she was in a coma, she looked like she'd wake up if I just leaned across and nudged her.

I suppose I should have stayed with my mum all

night. I reckon any normal person on hearing their mum was gonna die wouldn't even contemplate leaving her side. Instead, I arranged to go out for the night with my friend. You've gotta believe me when I say I was sure that those doctors were wrong and that my mum was gonna be okay. So I decided I'd go out and see her in the morning. Anyway, it was pretty fucking depressing being sat at someone's bedside in that hospital for hours, I can tell you. I wanted to go out and have a few drinks and try and get some girl. I didn't want to think about my mum or about the things we'd been told. My sister didn't say anything afterwards but she probably thought I was some kind of sicko by going out and not staying with my mum that night. She's probably right.

I went out for a few drinks with my friend later that night and went to a bar, before going onto a club. During the night, I'd told my mate what the doctor had said and he was all apologetic and stuff. That was nice but I just wanted him to stop going on about it so we could forget things and just concentrate on enjoying ourselves. To be completely honest though, I really didn't enjoy myself. I tried not to dwell on my mum or anything and I attempted to have a good time but I couldn't. I thought I'd feel better if I was absolutely wasted but I swear I just couldn't get drunk. I had loads and I still felt pretty fucking sober and I'm usually a real lightweight when it comes to that sort of thing.

After the club, I stayed at my friend's house as he didn't live too far from the hospital. I didn't sleep that great. It would have been difficult enough to get some decent shut-eye after the day I'd had but it was even more difficult attempting to sleep on a sofa half my size. I was up well before eight the next morning and so got dressed, had a wash, and then made my way across to the hospital. I was really hung over, I'd hardly slept and I was dressed in the previous day's clothes. I must have looked worse than any of the poor fuckers in that hospital, and there was nothing wrong with me.

When I got to my mum, she was still in exactly the same place and looked exactly the same as when I'd left her. I remembered that when the doctor told us about the coma, he'd said that we should still talk to her, even though it looked like she wasn't responding. When I remembered that, then I felt even worse about not staying with her. I told her I was sorry about leaving her although I didn't actually have a good explanation why I'd done it. I don't even know if she heard my apology anyway.

My sister turned up at the hospital shortly after, followed by my dad and uncle who joined us later on that morning. Not long after they'd arrived, one of the doctors took us in a separate room again. It was a different doctor to the one we'd previously seen, but he still had that solemn expression on his face – the same as the other doctor had. They must teach them how to do that look at medical school, I reckon.

Anyway, this new doctor explained that my mum wasn't showing any signs of improvement. He went on to say that it was now their opinion that the machine should be turned off. Apparently, it was the only thing that had been keeping my mum alive. He said she wasn't responding and was totally reliant on that machine. That got my sister really upset again. I didn't say anything 'cos I still didn't believe that they'd got it right. I mean, people aren't just fine one minute and dead the next. I kept thinking that somebody was gonna come in and tell us that there'd been a mistake and that she was okay. Nobody came though.

The nurses explained that we could go and have a few minutes with our mum for the last time, if we wanted to. My sister was too upset though. She was getting all hysterical and so my dad just took her away. After they left, I told the nurses that I'd like to go and sit with my mum. I'd have been ok on my own but my uncle came along with me anyway. He was the same uncle that had taken me to football all those years ago and had let my mum stay in all the houses that he'd owned. He was a great guy. On the surface, he didn't appear to be getting upset but when I looked into his eyes, I could see that he was hurting. I guess that he was just trying to hold it together for my sake.

We walked back to the ward and went and sat in the same seats by her bed. A nurse came and drew the curtains around us, although I didn't quite understand why. I just assumed it was to give us more privacy. My mum still looked exactly the same as earlier that morning and exactly the same as the day before that. She looked like she was just peacefully sleeping. They'd obviously got it wrong. She didn't look *at all* like somebody who was about to die.

After a few minutes, another nurse appeared through the curtains. She didn't say anything and just leant across and did something to the machine that they'd said was keeping my mum alive. Then she disappeared back through the drawn curtains and left us sat there in complete silence.

We remained sat in those uncomfortable plastic hospital chairs, watching my mum sleeping. Every so often, my uncle would ask if I was okay and I'd answer that I was. I really didn't feel that sad, to be honest. I *still* don't think I had accepted what they had told us.

I'm not sure how long we continued to sit staring at my mum. It seemed quite a while although it probably wasn't more than ten or so minutes. We sat largely in silence with the only noise emanating from elsewhere on the ward with the occasional sound of another patient talking, or a nurse pushing a trolley past the curtains. I shifted my chair forwards a little so that I could reach over and grab hold of one of my mum's hands. She still looked really serene and her hand was warm, just like it usually felt. At that exact moment, it was quiet and peaceful and everything was fine. A minute later, I was watching my mum die in front of me.

The next thing that happened was horrific and it made me wish I'd never asked to come and sit back with my mum. It made me wish I'd just left at the same time as my dad and sister. I remember I still had hold of her hand and she was still sleeping when, all of a sudden, this bright yellow gunk started dribbling out of my mum's mouth. I didn't know what was happening and didn't have a clue what that liquid was. It was really bright yellow – even more yellow than those fucking trainers. Seeing that fluid come out of my mum's mouth like that really upset me and I started crying. It wasn't so much that I was sad or anything, it was more 'cos of the shock of seeing that yellow stuff. It was like she was suffering or something and I felt fucking helpless.

I mean, they could have fucking *told* us that was going to happen. If they'd have told us what to expect then it wouldn't have been such a shock and I might not have gotten so upset. The nurses heard me wailing and came rushing through the curtains and asked us to leave them with her for a minute. I was *really* fucking upset. I felt like she needed help, but there was nothing I could do. I don't know why they didn't tell us about that yellow stuff.

We were sat outside the ward in the corridor and I calmed down quickly, 'cos I didn't like it that people were looking at me. It's fucking crazy but even after everything those doctors had told us, and even after seeing them turning off that machine and seeing all that yellow stuff come out of my mum's mouth, I still didn't think she was dead. I mean, I *knew* she was dead, but I suppose I just didn't believe it. If she'd been really ill with some terminal illness or something for weeks on end, then maybe I might have been able to accept it but, like I said, she'd looked fine lying in that bed. And she'd been talking to us just a couple of days earlier.

It's not fair.

It's really not *fucking* fair.

Chapter Twenty-One

I can't even remember the last conversation I had with my mum. To be honest, I probably wasn't paying any fucking attention when she *was* talking to me. I would've done though, if I'd known it was the last time I would be able to talk to her. I would've listened to every word she said and I would have told her loads of stuff, like how much I love her. I just didn't know though.

Things were made worse in the aftermath of my mum's death 'cos it was pretty fucking obvious that the hospital was culpable by not spotting what was wrong with her when she was initially admitted. If they'd spotted that tear in her bowel on the x-ray and not just sent her home, then she wouldn't have been poisoned for the length of time that she was. And if she hadn't been poisoned for the length of time that she was, she might still be alive today. We weren't really in the mood to get caught up in a load of legal nonsense, but the solicitors encouraged us to pursue a case of negligence against the hospital anyway. Obviously, the hospital vehemently denied any wrongdoing and even dredged up all my mum's old hospital files. They were trying to make out she was some suicidal nutcase even though it was totally un-*fucking*-related to the condition that killed her. They offered us fifteen thousand pounds to settle the case out of court on the proviso that they wouldn't accept any liability for my mum's death. The solicitor said we could press on through the courts, but there was no guarantee we would win and she advised that it might end up costing us lots of money that we didn't have. I really didn't care about the money and wanted to pursue those bastards through the courts until they admitted wrongdoing. We settled though – largely because my sister was a single mum with two young kids and that money helped her out quite a bit. I still feel a bit regretful that we didn't continue the fight. I didn't want their money and I would have been happy with nothing. I just wanted them to say sorry.

I really don't feel like going on about this stuff anymore. You're probably sick of me by now anyway, what with me moaning on like this. To be honest, it's making *me* feel pretty fucking depressed again now. I guess it's been alright telling you all this stuff though, 'cos I don't really like talking to people about this kind of thing. I should have just told you about that hospital stuff ages ago, and I think that was my intention when I started. I guess I wasn't looking forward to it, so I just put it off and told you about loads of other crap instead.

It's been good talking to you though, it really has.

About The Author

Neil Calcutt resides in Manchester, England. *Reader Meet Author* is his debut novel. His second novel, *The Grotesquely Lonely*, is waiting in the wings.

Reference List

Wilde, R. and Wilde, M. (1981). Kids in America [Lyrics].
Label: RAK Records.
In Text: Pgs 144/145

"Being brought up in a barber's shop is not the only similarity that our hero has with Kenneth Williams. The at times sharp but never gratuitously cruel humour, the self deprecating asides and the sheer brilliance of transposing the everyday mundane and humdrum into a comedic tale delivered with the skill of a born raconteur is also reminiscent of the sadly departed comedian. It should be noted that imitation is not the sincerest form of flattery - originality of the same high standard is."

"I LOVE this book. Really funny. Really made me smile."

"A conveyor belt of great lines crammed in here. I really like the rueful, irreverent, observational type of humour. From experience, I know publishers and agents are loath to entertain anything resembling a 'Misery Memoir', but I think this has captured something that transcends that particular pigeonhole."

"Funny and moving. This is a book that a lot of people will identify with."

"Humorous and earthy, and will appeal to the many readers who don't read "true-life stories". Its moments of pathos are much more effective for being leavened by humour."

"This is comic and as much about the personality of the narrator as about his life experiences. I laughed many times while reading."

"Brilliant - you struck an awful lot of nails on the head with this one. I like the way your weariness at the start gives way to blistering cynicism. Hilarious - and somewhat scary - ruminations on the stuff of life and death. Great stuff"

"Ha. How could I not enjoy this? This is some of the most honest, poignant and funny stuff. It's honest, it's real, it's very English, but universal. Would Morrissey approve? Yep, I think he would. I certainly do."